NATIONAL GALLERY CATALOGUES

THE
GERMAN SCHOOL

BY
MICHAEL LEVEY

D1401156

PUBLISHED BY ORDER OF THE TRUSTEES

PUBLICATIONS DEPT
THE NATIONAL GALLERY
LONDON

MCMLIX

Made and printed in Great Britain by William Clowes and Sons, Limited, London and Beccles

FOREWORD

THIS CATALOGUE deals with all German and Austrian pictures in the National Gallery, and also with any pictures in the Collection which may be claimed as Swiss. Pictures by artists of these nationalities who worked largely abroad (*e.g.* Elsheimer) are included.

At the end of the catalogue is a list of the pictures included here as well as a list of attributions changed from the 1929 catalogue and 1939 supplement. In Appendix II is printed the relevant part of the Christie sale catalogue of 1857 showing those German pictures which once belonged to the Gallery.

My first and most considerable debt of gratitude is to my colleagues Mr. Martin Davies and Mr. Neil MacLaren. For a number of pictures catalogued here they had, over a period of years, drafted entries which they generously placed at my disposal. I hope I have benefited from their scholarship. In most cases what is printed here is longer than those draft entries; and for the opinions expressed here I alone am responsible. I owe a further debt of gratitude to Mr. Davies for so kindly consenting to the transfer to this catalogue of his entries for the two pictures by Holbein, published in the British School catalogue of 1946. For the purposes of the present catalogue they have been slightly redrafted, but the scholarship of them remains his.

I owe many other debts of gratitude and I hope specific instances are acknowledged in their place. Messrs. Christie, Manson and Woods have once again been unfailingly helpful over sales. At the Rijksbureau voor Kunsthistorische Documentatie, Dr. H. Gerson has not only kindly helped me over sales but also over books not obtainable in England. At the Witt Library of the Courtauld Institute, Dr. P. Murray has helped me in many ways. I am particularly grateful for the kindness and help given me by Dr. Paul Pieper at Münster, and at Nuremberg by Dr. Peter Strieder. For encouragement, and for opportunities to discuss some of the pictures catalogued here, I am also indebted to Mr. J. Byam Shaw, Professor L. D. Ettlinger, and Mr. Christopher White.

At the Gallery, I owe a debt of gratitude to Miss Joyce Plesters, Experimental Officer, who has taken many paint sections and wood samples for me; to the Chief Restorer, Mr. A. W. Lucas, and the staff of the Restoration Department for much helpful advice; and to Mrs. V. Wilson and the Photographic Staff whose work has so often made mine much easier. Many of the pictures catalogued here raise, in one way or another, technical problems. I am gratefully aware of the contribution made by scientific and technical means to any solutions which are attempted here.

All the pictures in this catalogue have been photographed and will be reproduced in the companion volume of German School Plates which is already at the printer and will be published shortly.

MICHAEL LEVEY

The present volume is one of a series produced under the editorship of the Keeper to replace the catalogue of 1929.

EXPLANATIONS

CONDITION: Unless the contrary is stated, all original canvases may be taken as having been relined. The notes on condition refer to the state of the pictures at the time of writing; later cleaning may make some of these notes obsolete. When a picture has been cleaned fairly recently a note to that effect is added.

MEASUREMENTS: All the pictures in this catalogue have been re-measured and, as should be clear, the area of the painted surface is given. The size is quoted in inches, followed by metres in brackets. Height precedes width.

RIGHT AND LEFT: Unless otherwise implied by the context, these refer to the spectator's right and left.

ABBREVIATIONS: The titles of most books are referred to in full. An exception is U. Thieme and F. Becker, *Allgemeines Lexikon der bildenden Künstler* . . . , 1907–50, which is cited as: Thieme-Becker *Lexikon*, with relevant volume number. The edition used of J. B. Rietstap, *Armorial Général*, is that of 1950 sqq. often quoted here simply as Rietstap. Periodical titles are usually quoted in full, except *Jahrbuch der (Königlich) Preuszischen Kunstsammlungen* and *Jahrbuch der Kunsthistorischen Sammlungen (des Allerhöchsten Kaiserhauses)* which appear as Prussian *Jahrbuch* and Vienna *Jahrbuch* respectively. Where the name of a city is given in brackets after mention of a picture, the picture is in the principal public gallery of that city.

AUGSBURG(?) School, XVI century

2604 PORTRAIT OF A MAN

Poplar, 15 × 11⅛ (0·381 × 0·283).
Considerably worn and repainted; in general the condition is unreliable. A *pentimento* in the thumb of the sitter's left hand.

The picture was for long attributed to Amberger and appears thus in the 1929 catalogue. However, Weizsäcker early rejected the attribution and suggested the vague possibility of the picture being by Niklaus Manuel Deutsch.[1] Feulner later republished it as by Amberger,[2] which is certainly wrong and was in fact pointedly rejected again by Baldass.[3] Buchner has associated No. 2604 with the Nuremberg School, particularly with a pair of portraits of Johann Neudörfer and his wife, at Cassel.[4]

Although not by Amberger, No. 2604 seems to the present writer much more typical of Augsburg work than Nuremberg work of the same period. P. Strieder (verbal) agrees with this opinion. A date of *ca.* 1530 for the execution is in any case likely.

PROVENANCE: Said to be from the Leyland collection.[5] Bought by George Salting in 1893[6]; lent to the exhibition at the Royal Academy, 1895 (no. 177); from that year on loan to the National Gallery. Salting Bequest, 1910.

REPRODUCTION: *Illustrations, Continental Schools*, 1937, p. 7.

REFERENCES: (1) Cf. his review of the 1895 R.A. exhibition (see under Provenance) in *Repertorium für Kunstwissenschaft*, XVIII, 1895, p. 217. (2) *Beiträge zur Geschichte der deutschen Kunst*, II, 1928, p. 447. (3) *Pantheon*, IX, 1932, p. 184, note 2. Friedländer's oral agreement that the picture is not by Amberger is recorded in a note of the same year in the Gallery archives. (4) See P. Strieder in *Münchner Jahrbuch . . .*, VII, 1956, p. 124, note 13. The Cassel portraits are reproduced by Strieder, *loc. cit.*, figs. 4–5. (5) So Weizsäcker, *loc. cit.* There seems no other reference to the picture as in the Leyland collection; No. 2604 was not in the sale of 1892 though it may have become available at that date. (6) Note in the Salting MSS. (in the Gallery archives).

AUSTRIAN School, XV century

3662 THE TRINITY WITH CHRIST CRUCIFIED

The back of the panel painted with a pattern of green leaves on a white ground.[1]

Silver fir (*abies alba*), painted area, 46½ × 45¼ (1·181 × 1·15) within an original gold framing at the top and sides; the bottom is a modern replacement. It can be presumed that the bottom edge of the panel has been cut, and some evidence for this is the abrupt breaking off of the pattern at this edge.

In general in good condition. There are some paint losses, most obviously in the angels' wings and at the base of the Cross. Some wearing in the gold background.

The Trinity is depicted as a Throne of Mercy image (the *Gnaden-stuhl*), particularly common in Northern art. A number of comparable Austrian depictions exist, but few on the scale of No. 3662.[2]

The picture was first published by Holmes[3] who recorded that it was once ascribed to the Avignon School but had also been associated with the School of the Bodensee. His conclusions were that No. 3662 was French in origin; it appears in the 1929 catalogue as Franco-Rhenish, fifteenth century. It was attributed by van Marle[4] to Hermann Wynrich von Wesel, whom he agreed with Firmenich-Richartz in identifying as the Master of S. Veronica (*q.v.*).

It is now generally recognized that the picture is in fact of Austrian origin and very closely related to pictures painted in Styria in the early part of the fifteenth century. Suida recorded that he first saw No. 3662 in 1922 and recognized it as Austrian.[5] The specific association seems to have been published first by Hugelshofer,[6] dating the picture *ca.* 1410. By Pächt[7] it was at one time attributed to the Master of S. Lambrecht (now often identified as Hans von Tübingen), with whose style it has many analogies.

The picture has been discussed a great deal in literature, and probably not all the references to it are recorded here. The tendency since Hugelshofer has been to isolate No. 3662 and attribute it to an individual master, influenced by the S. Lambrecht Master, and possibly active at Vienna. Suida saw no grounds for supposing the picture Viennese; he dated it in the twenties and drew attention to its Styrian and Bohemian elements.[8] Baldass emphasized that No. 3662 was by a different hand from the S. Lambrecht votive picture (after which the S. Lambrecht Master is named).[9] Benesch distinguished it from the Linz Master.[10] Oettinger argued for a later date of origin, in the second quarter of the fifteenth century.[11] Recently Baldass has returned to the question and, rejecting Oettinger's dating, has pointed out that the treatment of the draperies in No. 3662 suggests an earlier period.[12]

No. 3662 is sometimes made the key work of a 'Master of the London Throne of Mercy' to whom a few other pictures are attributed.[13] Some further references are under the biography for that reconstructed personality in this catalogue.

The panel of No. 3662 has hinge marks at both sides, indicating that it was originally an altarpiece with wings.[14] Grossmann first published four panels at Schloss Rastenberg which he later (unpublished) linked as the original wings of No. 3662.[15] He has apparently attributed the altarpiece to the Vienna School.[16] There is a slight discrepancy between the height of the proposed wings and that of the central panel, explicable by the likelihood that No. 3662 has been cut down at the bottom. The Rastenberg panels have recently been cleaned and the association of them with No. 3662 made by Demus.[17] The panels show: *S. Lawrence*;

S. Stephen(?); *Virgin and Child*; a Sainted Nun (a poor Clare?). Demus suggests that the *Virgin and Child* and *S. Stephen*, which seem of higher quality, were the inner wings, the other two saints the outer wings.

PROVENANCE: At one time in Switzerland[18]; with a dealer in Florence in 1921 (doubtfully as from Piedmont and to have belonged to a member of the Italian Royal Family[19]). Acquired thence by Cassirer, Berlin, whence purchased out of the Grant-in-aid, Temple West and Florence Funds, with a donation from the National Art-Collections Fund, 1922.

REPRODUCTION: *Illustrations, Continental Schools*, 1937, p. 128.

REFERENCES: (1) It is reproduced by Martin Davies, *Paintings and Drawings on the Backs of National Gallery Pictures*, 1946, pl. 36. (2) For some specific parallels, cf. O. Benesch in Vienna *Jahrbuch*, 1928, p. 69. For some general literature on the subject, see the note 2 under Baldung No. 1427 of this catalogue. (3) In *The Burlington Magazine*, XLI, 1922, pp. 76 ff. (4) See his article in *Art in America*, vol. XI, 1923, pp. 123 ff. (5) W. Suida, *Österreichs Malerei in der Zeit Erzherzog Ernst des Eisernen und König Albrecht II*, 1926, p. 24. (6) See his article in *Beiträge zur Geschichte der deutschen Kunst*, I, 1924, pp. 21 ff. (7) O. Pächt, *Österreichische Tafelmalerei der Gotik*, 1929, p. 69. (8) Suida, *loc. cit.* (9) L. Baldass in *Cicerone*, 1929, pp. 67-8. His note 1, p. 68, rightly corrects the comments of Hugelshofer on the colours of No. 3662. (10) O. Benesch in Vienna *Jahrbuch*, 1930, p. 167. Additionally, the picture is commented on, as School of Vienna, by K. T. Parker in *Old Master Drawings*, vol. I, 1926, p. 24. See also G. Ring, *A Century of French Painting, 1400-1500*, 1949, no. 28, rejecting Burgundian and Rhenish associations and attributing the picture to a painter in the entourage of the S. Lambrecht Master. This seems particularly prompted by the appearance of No. 3662 as French in J. Evans, *Art in Medieval France, 987-1498*, 1948, fig. 200: cf. E. Panofsky, *Early Netherlandish Painting*, 1953, I, p. 387 (note 1 to p. 67). (11) K. Oettinger in Vienna *Jahrbuch*, 1936, p. 86, also the same author, *Hans von Tübingen und seine Schule*, 1938, pp. 73 ff. (12) See his article in *Wiener Jahrbuch für Kunstgeschichte*, 1953, p. 10, note 9. (13) See the discussion in K. Oettinger, *Hans von Tübingen und seine Schule*, 1938, pp. 69 ff. (14) It is also slotted at both sides, but the purpose of this is not clear. (15) F. Grossmann in *Belvedere*, XI, 1932, pp. 51 ff. Notes of 1941 and 1947 in the Gallery archives refer to his linking of the Rastenberg panels with No. 3662. (16) Notes in the Gallery archives. (17) Letter of 1952 from O. Demus in the Gallery archives; photographs of the Rastenberg panels also in the Gallery archives. (18) A Swiss customs stamp, at Lucerne, on the back. (19) This seems very far from established. Van Marle, *loc. cit.*, p. 123, says when he saw the picture in Florence it was said to have been for many years in a small village near Florence. According to a letter of 1922, from Cassirer's, the picture turned up in Florence in 1921 as by Lochner and was then said to be from a member of the Italian Royal Family in Turin. On the back of No. 3662, a label with some figures, a word partly illegible and 'Pala d'oro'.

HANS BALDUNG GRIEN
1484/5–1545

The date of birth is deducible from a distich printed under a woodcut portrait of the artist in *Epicedion Thomae Sporei* (Strasbourg) 1534 [1]; it corrects the previous supposition, which is still at times repeated, of 1476. The place of Baldung's birth remains doubtful; conceivably it was Weyersheim, near Strasbourg, but more probably it was Gmünd in Swabia whence the family certainly came. The *Coronation of the Virgin*

(of 1516) on the high altar of the cathedral at Freiburg is inscribed with
Baldung's name thus: *Joannes Baldung Cog. Grien Gamundianus.* . . .

Baldung's early training is obscure. He may be supposed to have
worked first at Strasbourg where Schongauer's influence would be felt.
He is usually said to have worked at an early period (*i.e.* pre-1505) in
Dürer's studio at Nuremberg. It should be emphasized that the evidence
for this is purely stylistic. Dürer refers to Baldung twice very briefly in
1521 during his Netherlandish journey; but these entries prove nothing.[2]

The first known dated painting is the *S. Sebastian* altarpiece of 1507
for the Stadtkirche at Halle (now in the Germanisches Nationalmuseum,
Nuremberg). Signed and dated pictures occur from then onwards at
intervals throughout his career. He is first recorded at Strasbourg in the
following year, by which time he was married. He was first active for
the Margrave Christopher I of Baden, *ca.* 1510–11 (votive picture of the
Margrave and family now in the Kunsthalle, Carlsruhe). Other com-
missions from the Baden court followed.

He is first recorded at Freiburg-im-Breisgau in May 1512.[3] There are
yearly references to him there thence onwards until 1517. He was
engaged chiefly on work for the cathedral, executing pictures and de-
signing stained glass (still *in situ*). In 1517 he regained his citizenship at
Strasbourg, where he settled. He died at Strasbourg, September 1545.[4]

REFERENCES: **(1)** Discovered by C. Koch; cf. *Zeitschrift für Kunstgeschichte*
1933, pp. 34 ff. **(2)** H. Curjel, *Hans Baldung Grien*, 1923, pp. 146 ff., for what
can be said about Baldung's relations with Dürer. It need not be supposed that
Dürer's reference to 'Hans Grun' shows a particular intimacy, as Baldung is
referred to similarly in Viator (Jean Pelerin), *De artificiosa perspectiva*, III, of
the same year, as well as elsewhere. It is quite true that later Baldung owned a
lock of Dürer's hair (see Escherich, cited in note 4 below, p. 28) but that does
not prove a great deal. **(3)** Exhaustive discussion of the period is in H. Perseke,
Hans Baldungs Schaffen in Freiburg, 1941, superseding previous studies. **(4)** A
brief but up-to-date study of Baldung is O. Fischer, *Hans Baldung Grien*, 1943
ed. See also the catalogue of the Baldung exhibition, Carlsruhe, 1959. The
majority of early references to Baldung is in M. Escherich, *Hans Baldung-Grien
Bibliographie 1509–1515*, 1916; see also H. Rott in *Quellen und Forschungen zur
Kunstgeschichte im XV. und XVI. Jahrhundert*, III, *Der Oberrhein*, 1936, I.

245 PORTRAIT OF A MAN

Suspended from the lower chain about his neck two badges in gold:
the Virgin half-length holding the Child, in a crescent moon with rays;
a fish and falcon on a branch, separated by a crossed sword and club.

Dated at the top: *1514*.

Lime, painted surface, $23\frac{5}{8} \times 19\frac{1}{4}$ (0·593 × 0·49).

Probably slightly cut at the bottom where only a trace remains of the
sitter's puffed shirt; perhaps his left hand was originally included in the
picture.

In general in good condition, despite some damage caused by cracking.
There is a damage in the area of the fish which until recent cleaning had
been repainted as another falcon (some further comment is below). At the
time of cleaning a false Dürer monogram was removed. Cleaned in 1957.

The sitter has sometimes been identified as a Margrave of Baden (cf. Gallery catalogues of 1920 and 1925) presumably because of a vague resemblance to the Margrave Christopher I who was also painted by Baldung. Baumgarten suggested that the sitter might be some member of the Baden margravine house, possibly Bernard III, eldest son of Christopher I.[1] The similarity is again superficial, and the sitter of No. 245 must be more than forty years old, which was Bernard III's age in 1514. Previously No. 245 has been called a 'Senator', but the title is meaningless.

The Virgin and Child badge which he wears is part of the insignia of the order of Our Lady of the Swan. As a confraternity in honour of the Virgin, the order was founded by the Elector Frederick II of Brandenburg on Michaelmas Day, 1440. The statutes of it as the Swan order were issued on the feast of the Assumption, 1443.[2] The badge is often shown worn as here, without the additional pendant of the Swan itself [3]; but in those cases it is usually suspended from the very distinctive collar of the order, a chain of hearts between saw blades. The crescent moon of the original badge bore the words 'Ave mundi Domina',[4] but the detail has been omitted by Baldung. Despite the plain chain worn by the sitter of No. 245, it is reasonable to suppose he is a member of the Swan order. Men and women of noble birth were admitted to the order, which was religious rather than chivalrous in intention. Originally restricted in numbers, it soon had a very large membership; a perhaps unique feature was that the order was inheritable.

The fish and falcon badge seems to be that of the Swabian Fish and Falcon jousting company (one of the *Turniergesellschaften*). Ganz had already proposed this long before the picture was cleaned,[5] and the badge as previously restored made no sense. In another sixteenth-century male portrait the sitter wears the badge in his hat[6]; a collar of the company, formed of interlinked badges, is shown by Schaffner worn by a female as well as male sitter in the *Anwyl Epitaph* of 1514 (Stuttgart). Originally the Fish and Falcon were separate companies, amalgamated apparently in 1484.[7]

Scheibler seems the first who pointed out that No. 245 was by Baldung, not Dürer as it had previously been called.[8] The date, as opposed to the monogram on the picture, had always seemed genuine[9] and this was confirmed by cleaning.

PROVENANCE: In the E. Joly de Bammeville sale, London, 12 June 1854 (lot 35),[10] bought for the National Gallery.

REPRODUCTION: *Illustrations, Continental Schools*, 1937, p. 14.

REFERENCES: General: G. von Térey, *Verzeichnis der Gemälde des Hans Baldung gen. Grien*, 1894, no. 32.

In text: (1) See F. Baumgarten, *Der Freiburger Hochaltar*, 1904, p. 9, note 24. (2) These dates are taken from Rudolph, Freiherr von Stillfried-Rattonitz, *Der Schwanenorden*, 1845 ed.; documents of foundation printed by him, *op. cit.*, pp. 29 ff. (3) For instance, by the kneeling man in armour prominently at the right in Dürer's *Allerheiligenbild* (Vienna). Examples of the complete order are many in pictures; cf., for example, *Sibylla von Freyberg* by Strigel (Munich).

(4) Stillfried-Rattonitz, *op. cit.*, p. 7. (5) P. Ganz in *Schweizerisches Archiv für Heraldik*, 1905–6, p. 36. Dr. Otto Kurz very kindly drew attention to this article. Ganz reproduced (*loc. cit.*, fig. 55) a drawing after the badge in No. 245 purporting to represent it. What that sketch shows is what should, and in fact now does, appear in the picture. (6) Strigel's portrait of Johann Caspar von Laubenberg, at Carlsruhe: for which further see J. Lauts, *Altdeutsche Meister aus der staatlichen Kunsthalle*..., 1958, no. 26. A portrait of a man by Baldung (Bâle) with Fish and Falcon badge in the upper left-hand corner, reproduced by H. Curjel, *Hans Baldung Grien*, 1923, pl. 54. (7) The date is from O. Eberbach, *Die deutsche Reichritterschaft in ihrer staatsrechtlich-politischen Entwicklung* ..., 1913, p. 98. In fact they seem amalgamated for a tournament of 1481, according to Rüxner's *Thurnierbuch*, 1628, pp. clxxxix ff.; but the point is of no importance for No. 245. (8) So Térey, cited in general reference above. (9) Unjustifiable doubt is cast on it by the 1929 catalogue. (10) As by Dürer.

1427 THE TRINITY AND MYSTIC PIETÀ

Christ supported in the tomb by God the Father, the Virgin and S. John. Above them the Dove. Below the tomb kneeling figures of the donor(?) and his family(?) with two coats-of-arms (discussed below).

Signed along the parapet of the tomb: ·HBG· (in monogram) *BALDVᴚG 1512*

Oak, painted surface, 44$\frac{3}{8}$ × 35$\frac{1}{8}$ (1·123 × 0·891).

In general in good condition under discoloured varnish, despite the cracks in the panel. The gold on the haloes is new.

The subject is not uncommon in linking the Trinity and the Passion, but it is much less usual for the Virgin or for S. John to accompany such a scene.[1] The iconography of the Trinity and Passion depiction has been quite extensively discussed, but there are conflicting views on the origin of the subject.[2] This type of mystic Pietà, where God the Father becomes a mourner, was particularly popular in the Netherlands and Germany. However, it is doubtful if there exist more than one or two pictures with iconography exactly similar to that of No. 1427. There is some general derivation of the subject from earlier treatments of the Trinity with Christ crucified (of which No. 3662 of this catalogue, Austrian School, is an example); the unusual feature of the picture is that this motive should be conflated with the ordinary Pietà subject of Christ in the tomb supported by the Virgin and S. John.[3]

The date on No. 1427 would anyway suggest it was probably painted at Strasbourg, and the two coats-of-arms seem to be those of Strasbourg families: exactly which is a doubtful matter. The shields were identified first by von Térey, and as of the Bettschold and Rothschild families.[4] Pariset, who has discussed the problem in some detail,[5] also recognized in the left-hand shield the arms of the Bettschold family which he gives as: *trois têtes de cerf sur fond noir*. However, the field of the shield in No. 1427 is not *sable* but *azure*; varnish has obscured the original colour. But despite this slip the shield is correctly identified with the Bettschold arms, which are given by Rietstap as: *D'azur à trois têtes de cerf d'or*.

For the other arms Pariset proposed the families either of Heilmann or Wilhelm. What is shown in the picture records better with those of

Heilmann, as given by Rietstap: *D'azur à la fasce d'or, accompagné de trois coquilles de gueules et d'or.*

The donors tentatively suggested by Pariset were Adelaide Rotschilt-Wilhelm who married a Frederick Bettscholt in 1500. Pariset notes that no alliance is recorded between the families of Bettschold and Heilmann, but he also produced some evidence to make his own identifications doubtful.[6]

An additional problem is raised by the male donor left of centre. His dress indicates that he is a canon and presumably of the Bettschold family. According to Pariset, he might be any one of four members of the family, no less than three of whom were canons of S. Pierre-le-Vieux at Strasbourg. There can be no doubt that the canon in the picture is very prominently shown and might well seem the most likely person to be the donor. His relationship to the other persons in the picture would then be rather uncertain. The present writer has not been able to add any clarification to the points discussed by Pariset, except to doubt if Adelaide Rotschilt-Wilhelm is shown in the picture, on the evidence of the shields.

The chief interest and importance of identifying the donor or donors in No. 1427 would be to establish its provenance. At present it can be said only that it is most likely to come from a church at Strasbourg and that conceivably this church was S. Pierre-le-Vieux.

COPY: A drawing after No. 1427 (omitting all the composition below the parapet of the tomb) is at Poitiers.[7]

PROVENANCE: Recorded in the collection of Dr. Richard Farmer, Cambridge, by May 1777.[8] Dr. Farmer sale, London, 7 May 1798 (lot 58).[9] Lent by A. F. Payne to the Royal Academy exhibition, 1891 (no. 165). Bought from the restorer Carter by Sir George Donaldson,[10] from whom purchased at cost price, out of the Lewis Fund, 1894.

REPRODUCTION: *Illustrations, Continental Schools*, 1937, p. 14.

REFERENCES: *General:* G. von Térey, *Verzeichnis der Gemälde des Hans Baldung gen. Grien*, 1894 (no. 53), from a photograph and as of unknown location. See also G. von Térey in *Repertorium für Kunstwissenschaft*, 1895, p. 473.
In text: (1) A somewhat similar composition by Baldung is at Bâle. (2) See the discussion in E. Mâle, *L'Art Religieux de la Fin du Moyen-Age en France*, 1922 ed., pp. 140 ff. The evolution of the subject is no doubt from the Gnadenstuhl type of Trinity, recorded as early as in a window placed by Abbot Suger in Saint-Denis (in an approximate form only) and at least as late as J. van Bijlert; cf. J. J. M. Timmers, *Symboliek en Iconographie der Christelijke Kunst*, 1947, pp. 71 and 74; Bijlert's picture there, pl. 2. Some further detailed discussion, and some representations, in K. Smits, *Het Gilderboek*, Oct. 1936, pp. 125 ff. (Netherlandish art); see also G. Troescher in *Wallraf-Richartz Jahrbuch*, 1936, pp. 148 ff. In addition may be mentioned a very elaborate Gnadenstuhl by the Master of the Virgo inter Virgines at Agram published by G. von Térey in *The Burlington Magazine*, L, 1927, pp. 297–8; and the Gnadenstuhl on the obverse of the so-called 'Moritzpfennig' of 1544 with its supporting quotation from Isaiah liii, 8. (3) The Pietà subject as treated by Schongauer perhaps had some influence on Baldung's treatment in No. 1427; for the point see H. Haug's article in *Archives Alsaciennes*, 1932, pp. 102–3. (4) In *Repertorium für Kunstwissenschaft*, cited under General references above. (5) In *L'Annuaire . . . du Club*

Vosgien, II, 1933 (off-print in the National Gallery archives). The coats-of-arms had previously been identified independently by A. van der Put as Bettschold and Heilmann (letter of 1933 in Gallery archives). Pariset points out, *loc. cit.*, the significance of the Bettschold coat-of-arms in connection with Baldung at Freiburg, since a member of the Bettschold family was married to Sebastian von Blumenegg. H. Perseke, *Hans Baldungs Schaffen in Freiburg*, 1941, p. 83, presumes that No. 1427 was the last picture painted by Baldung at Strasbourg before setting off in 1512 for Freiburg. (6) The difficulties can hardly be discussed briefly, but include the fact that the Frederick Bettschold in question married in 1500 and was dead by 1501 (a difficulty about the number of children shown in No. 1427) and that the Adelaide Rotschilt who married him may or may not be the person recorded as having married Theodor Bettschold (†1508) whose widow she is said to be at the time of her own death (1513). (7) A reproduction in the Poitiers catalogue, 1930, pl. 6 (no. 585). A photograph was kindly sent by Marc Sandoz who also drew attention to a note on the drawing by E. Schilling in the *Bulletin de la Société des Amis des Musées de Poitiers*, no. 5, Jan. 1952, p. 4, attributing the drawing to the South German School *ca.* 1600 and pointing out that the colours of the costumes are noted by the first letter of each adjective (in German). (8) See the letter printed by G. R. Owst, *Proceedings of the Cambridge Antiquarian Society*, XLII, 1949, p. 74, from the Rev. William Cole to Horace Walpole (18 May 1777) mentioning the picture as 'a new acquisition' of Dr. Farmer's; some further discussion by Owst, *loc. cit.* (9) Attention was drawn to this by Seymour de Ricci in *The Times Literary Supplement*, 4 Dec. 1924. (10) Letter of 1899 from Sir George Donaldson (in the Gallery archives).

BARTHOLOMEUS BRUYN the Elder
1492/3–1555

Probably born at Wesel, or else at Cologne.[1] The date of birth is deduced from a portrait medal of Bruyn by Hagenauer (dated 1539), where the subject's age is given as forty-six.[2] Bruyn is there called 'Pictor Coloniensis' and he is definitely recorded as a painter at Cologne by 1518 (when recorded in the painters' guild); an attributed but universally accepted *Triptych* (dated 1515) provides very strong presumptive evidence that he was already active at Cologne by that date.[3]

Two pairs of wings and two predellas for a reliquary high altarpiece in the cathedral at Essen are documented by a contract of 17 July 1522 [4] and are recorded as finished by 1525; of this only one pair of wings has survived. Wings of a high altarpiece for the cathedral at Xanten are documented by a contract of 22 April 1529 [5] and were completed by 1534 (a date on one panel of these); a lunette for the same altarpiece is probably of rather later date. There are no signed pictures, apparently. Bruyn died at Cologne, 1555.

On the basis of the Essen and Xanten altarpieces, a number of pictures are attributed (many dated). There are many portraits, in addition to religious pictures, and Bruyn's activity as a portraitist is recorded in some detail by one of his patrons, Hermann von Weinsberg.[6] Early work, such as the 1515 Triptych for Peter van Clapis, shows the influence of Jan Joest by whom Bruyn may have been trained.[7] The influence also on him of the Master of the Death of the Virgin, whose two important altarpieces were then in Cologne, is very marked. His later work shows awareness of such contemporaries as Jan Scorel. Bruyn's sons, Bartholomeus the Younger and Arnold, also worked as painters.

REFERENCES: (1) The evidence is virtually non-existent, but E. Firmenich-Richartz (Thieme-Becker, *Lexikon*, V, *ad vocem*) draws attention to a document where mention of 'Bartholomaeum Fuscum civem Coloniensem' is glossed 'natione Wesaliensem'; the relationship with Jan Joest (see note 7 below) is a further pointer to Wesel. (2) *Recto* and *verso* of the medal in E. Firmenich-Richartz, *Bartholomaeus Bruyn und seine Schule*, 1891, p. 7; for some further comment on it, see G. Habich in Prussian *Jahrbuch*, 1907, p. 257. (3) For this altarpiece, which contains portraits of Dr. Peter van Clapis and his wife (who lived at Cologne), see the Bruyn exhibition catalogue, Cologne, 1955 (2nd expanded edition), no. 142, with references to earlier literature. (4) See P. Clemen in *Repertorium für Kunstwissenschaft*, 1892, pp. 245 ff. (5) Compare J. J. Merlo, *Nachrichten von dem Leben und dem Werken kölnischer Künstler*, 1850, p. 72. (6) See E. Firmenich-Richartz, *Bartholomaeus Bruyn . . .*, 1891, pp. 17 ff. (7) The rather cryptic reference to their relationship as documented, in M. J. Friedländer, *Die Altniederländische Malerei*, IX, 1931, p. 61, is explained by F. Witte's discovery that the two painters were brothers-in-law; cf. F. Witte, *Quellen zur rheinischen Kunstgeschichte (Tausend Jahre deutscher Kunst am Rhein, V)*, 1931, p. 130, under Bruyn. Friedländer later expressed some doubt if, owing to the discrepancy in age, the two painters were actually brothers-in-law, cf. *op. cit.*, XIV, 1937, p. 114; also cf. C. P. Baudisch, *Jan Joest von Kalkar*, 1940, p. 13 on this point.

2605 A MAN OF THE STRAUSS(?) FAMILY

On the forefinger of his left hand the upper ring bears the arms: *de sable à la bande d'or, chargée de trois tourteaux de gueules*. In his right hand a paper inscribed: *das wortt gotzs | bleyptt inn ewygkaytt | esayas 40. capt.*

Oak, painted surface, $14\frac{1}{4} \times 9\frac{3}{4}$ (0·362 × 0·248); painted up to edges all round; possibly slightly cut down.

In general in quite good condition. There are many minor repaints covering cracks, especially in the flesh; a slight *pentimento* in the outline of the cap, also in the position of his left hand.

The English text of the inscription is: *The word of our God shall stand for ever* (Isaiah xl, 8). The text in German also occurs, in approximate form, on at least two sixteenth-century portrait medals.[1] The arms on the ring were identified by Firmenich-Richartz[2] as those of the Strauss family which are the same, except for crescents instead of torteaux; the very small scale would account for this error. The second ring also appears to have borne a coat-of-arms but it is now impossible to decipher this.

The sitter has previously been called Dr. Leonard Fuchsius, the botanist, an identification rightly doubted in the catalogue of the Bruyn exhibition, Cologne, 1955.[3] Conceivably a confusion arose with *Fuscus*, the Latin name for Bruyn.[4] A possible identification for the sitter, though he is perhaps too young, might be Andreas zum Kampe, called Struyss, Ratsherr at Cologne 1503–21. His daughter was painted by Bruyn, and that portrait bears the Strauss arms prominently.

Weizsäcker[5] suggested that the picture was early work, and there are affinities with the portrait of Johann von Reidt (dated 1525), at Berlin.

PROVENANCE: In the collection of the Marquis of Normanby. Later in the collection of Henry Wilkinson, Enfield; Wilkinson sale (after death), London, 21 April 1888 (lot 139),[6] bought by George Salting. Exhibited at the Burlington Fine Arts Club, 1892 (no. 52)[7] and at the Royal Academy, 1895 (no. 179); from 1895 on loan to the National Gallery; Salting Bequest, 1910.

REPRODUCTION: *Illustrations, Continental Schools*, 1937, p. 39.

REFERENCES: (1) For these cf. G. Habich, *Die deutschen Schaumünzen des XVI Jahrhunderts*, I (part I) 1929, no. 361; I (part 2) 1931, no. 1315. (2) In Thieme-Becker *Lexikon*, vol. V, p. 157, col. 2. The Strauss arms appear on the portrait by Bruyn of Anna Pilgrum, née Strauss (see further in text) in the Wallraf-Richartz Museum, Cologne, also in a picture in the S. Ursula cycle by Bruyn in the same museum; cf. Bruyn exhibition catalogue (either edition) Cologne, 1955, no. 136. (3) *Op. cit.*, no. 61 (p. 128). (4) This suggestion seems to have been proposed already somewhere in literature on the subject, but the exact reference has not been traced. (5) In *Repertorium für Kunstwissenschaft*, XVIII, 1895, p. 217 (wrongly in the 1955 Cologne exhibition catalogue as suggested by Gronau). (6) As by Holbein and of Sir Thomas More. The previous provenance of No. 2605 is quoted there. There is no reference to the picture as at Mulgrave Castle in, for example, *The Athenæum*, 1877, II, pp. 504 ff. (collection of the Marchioness of Normanby). Most of the Normanby pictures had been collected by Lord Mulgrave, Haydon's patron. (7) As by Bruyn, and so attributed thenceforward.

3903   THE VIRGIN, S. JOHN, S. MARY MAGDALENE AND A HOLY WOMAN

Oak, painted surface, $26\frac{3}{4} \times 19$ (0·68 × 0·483).

In good condition. The flesh areas are very slightly worn and made up in a few places, of which the Virgin's hands are the most obvious.

The picture seems to be the right-hand portion of a Pietà diptych of which the other half will have shown the dead Christ. A version of No. 3903, of approximately the same size and with only very minor differences, was at Dresden.[1] To judge from a photograph, there seems little to choose in quality between the two pictures, either or both of which could be partly studio work. For neither of them has the comparable left-hand portion apparently survived.

The scale of the figures is rather unusual in Bruyn's work and they seem to show some vaguely Italianate influence[2] (transmitted perhaps via Dutch artists). The Dresden picture was claimed by Scheibler as middle period work[3]; and the two pictures were placed in the middle thirties in the Bruyn exhibition catalogue, Cologne, 1955.[4]

VERSIONS: That previously at Dresden has already been referred to; it was destroyed during the 1939-45 war. A damaged studio copy is recorded as in an anonymous sale, Paris (Hotel Drouot), 30 May 1934 (lot 3).[5]

PROVENANCE: In the Howel Wiles (of Florence) Sale, London, 17 February 1894 (lot 37),[6] bought by Wagner.[7] Presented by Henry Wagner, 1924.

REPRODUCTION: *Illustrations, Continental Schools*, 1937, p. 40.

REFERENCES: (1) Dresden catalogue, 1930, no. 1966, as the right-hand portion of a Pietà diptych. (2) For some comment on this point in relation to the Dresden version, see E. Firmenich-Richartz in Thieme-Becker *Lexikon*, V, p. 156. For the types of the figures, but on a different scale, compare Bruyn's *Deposition* of about the same date in the Wallraf-Richartz Museum, Cologne: Cologne 1957 catalogue, no. 258. (3) Compare E. Firmenich-Richartz, *Bartholomaeus Bruyn und seine Schule*, 1891, p. 105. (4) See the catalogue cited, under nos. 180 and 180A. (5) Recorded by a note in the Gallery archives. (6) As by Bartolomäus Zeitbloom. (7) The provenance recorded in Henry Wagner's MSS. kindly communicated by Mr. Anthony Wagner; it is further recorded there that the picture was identified in 1906 as a (contemporary?) copy of the Dresden version.

COLOGNE School, XV century

2670 PORTRAIT OF A WOMAN

Bust length, facing left; she holds a rosary. At the left a glass beaker containing flowers.

Oak, painted surface, $15\frac{1}{8} \times 11\frac{1}{4}$ (0.384 × 0.285); probably slightly cut down at top and bottom.

In good condition; there is slight wearing in the flesh and sky. *Pentimenti* in the upper outline of the headdress and the line of the veil where it crosses the face. Traces of under-drawing on the neck suggest that the hair was originally intended to extend as far as that. Cleaned in 1956.[1]

There are some minor unexplained oddities in the picture, such as the canopy behind the sitter and the details of her costume. It seems possible that the picture was part of a diptych (or even a triptych); it is unusual to find in comparable single portraits a canopy as in No. 2670. As far as can be judged from what remains at the top of the picture, the canopy projected above the sitter towards the left, *i.e.* the direction she faces.

The costume suggests a date *ca.* 1495 or a little later, but it is not very exactly paralleled in pictures of the period; a vaguely similar arrangement of hat and hair is worn by the Magdalen in the S. Thomas altarpiece at Cologne, by the Master of S. Bartholomew, and that picture is probably of about 1499 and anyway likely to be pre-1501.[2] The beaker at the left in No. 2670 is of a pattern of Rhenish glass, many fragments of which have been unearthed at Cologne.[3] An almost identical undamaged beaker is (or was) in the Kunstgewerbemuseum there,[4] and examples in other not necessarily German pictures seem to occur around 1500.

No. 2670, originally supposed to be Flemish, was ascribed to the French School by Hulin de Loo[5]; Friedländer's oral opinion that that was probable is recorded.[6] The suggestion that the picture was German appears to originate with Demonts (letter of 1927 in the Gallery archives); it was so catalogued in the 1929 catalogue, and the mention there of Strigel's influence is derived from a vague remark by Demonts. The handling of No. 2670 is in general typical of Cologne work towards the very end of the fifteenth century, and despite its minor oddities there is no reason to doubt its authenticity. There are some analogies in the handling with the younger Master of the Holy Kindred and it might even be claimed as close to him.[7] Nevertheless, the present writer feels that its quality is not high enough for this claim to be pressed.

PROVENANCE: In the collection of Léon de Somzée (†1901), Brussels. Lent by his sons C. and G. de Somzée to the exhibition, *Primitifs Flamands*, Bruges, 1902 (no. 231).[8] Acquired privately by George Salting, through Agnew, with some other Somzée pictures, 1902.[9] Salting Bequest, 1910.

REPRODUCTION: By W. Hausenstein, *Das Bild* . . . : 7, *Tafelmalerei der alten Franzosen*, 1923, pl. 77.[10]

REFERENCES: (1) At which time some false clouds were removed from the sky. (2) For this picture compare the Bartholomew Master's biography in this catalogue and see also Wallraf-Richartz Museum catalogue, 1957, p. 29 and pl. 23; no doubt, as usual with the Bartholomew Master, the costume is partly fantastic. Another similar headdress by him appears in the late *Deposition* in the Louvre, for which cf. the exhibition catalogue, *Des Maitres de Cologne à Albert Dürer*, Paris, 1950, pp. 55–6. (3) Further, cf. F. Rademacher in *Wallraf-Richartz Jahrbuch*, 1926–27, p. 102. (4) Rademacher, *loc. cit.*, fig. 15. At the time of writing (1957) the collections of the Kunstgewerbemuseum were not on exhibition. (5) *Catalogue Critique*, 1902, p. 62 (in connection with the Bruges exhibition, for which see under Provenance). (6) A note of 1932 in the Gallery archives. (7) There is for instance some similarity of handling between the donatrix in his *Pietà* in the Wallraf-Richartz Museum (no. 159) and No. 2670. (8) As by an unknown painter. Hulin's comment has already been quoted in the note 5 above. (9) Apparently as by Hugo van der Goes (so Salting MS. notebook in the Gallery archives); for some comment on the acquisition of these pictures see *The Connoisseur*, Nov. 1902, p. 203. (10) As by a Master *ca.* 1510.

LUCAS CRANACH the Elder
1472–1553

Born at Kronach (whence his name), in Upper Franconia: the date of birth is given by Matthias Gunderam.[1] By tradition a pupil there of his father, Hans. Probably *ca.* 1500, or slightly earlier, he was travelling through Bavaria and later reached Vienna. *The Crucifixion* (now Kunsthistorisches Museum, Vienna) is usually accepted as his earliest known painting. Taken into the service of the Elector Frederick of Saxony at Wittenberg, 14 April 1505,[2] and he remained there, working for the two successive Electors. Granted a patent to bear arms, 6 January 1508.[3] He was in the Netherlands in 1509.[4] He was elected a town councillor of Wittenberg in 1519 and was burgomaster there in 1537 and again in 1540. In 1550 he joined his patron the Elector John Frederick of Saxony at Augsburg,[5] where the Elector was the prisoner of Charles V. He painted Titian's portrait there, as recorded in his own accounts: '5 Florin vor Thucia [*sic*] Conterfet, des Malers von Venedig'.[6] He retired in 1552 to Weimar where he died, 16 October 1553.[7]

Cranach's activity was great and his studio output considerable. His sons Hans (†1537) and Lucas (1515–86) were certainly active in the studio; for Hans further see under No. 3922 below. The device of the flying snake or dragon, derived from Cranach's arms, was used indifferently on pictures from Cranach's own hand and on studio productions; it is often difficult, if not impossible, to mark the dividing line between the two. Studio participation cannot be totally excluded in the pictures catalogued as by him below, but it may be supposed to be unobtrusive.

REFERENCES: *General* M. J. Friedländer and J. Rosenberg, *Die Gemälde von Lucas Cranach*, 1932. A selection of the documents relating to Cranach published by W. Scheidig in *Lucas Cranach der Ältere* (Deutsche Akademie publication; various hands), 1953, pp. 156 ff.
In text: (1) See his biography of 1556, printed in J. Heller, *Das Leben und die Werke Lucas Cranach's*, 1844 ed., pp. 279 ff. (2) Scheidig, *op. cit.*, p. 156 (no. 1). For Cranach's activity under Frederick, see C. Gurlitt, *Die Kunst unter Kurfürst Friedrich dem Weisen*, 1897, pp. 40 ff. (3) The letter printed in C. Schuchardt, *Lucas Cranach . . .*, 1851, pp. 51 ff. (4) Schuchardt, *op. cit.*, pp. 57 ff. (5) Schuchardt, *op. cit.*, p. 195. (6) Following the text printed by Scheidig, *op. cit.*, p. 177 (no. 72). (7) The date on the gravestone: Schuchardt, *op. cit.*, p. 17.

291 PORTRAIT OF A WOMAN

Signed at the bottom left with Cranach's device. On the bodice of the woman's dress an embroidered pattern with the letter M.
Beech, $14\frac{1}{8} \times 9\frac{7}{8}$ (0.36×0.251).
Some obvious cracking but otherwise in good condition.

The quality of No. 291 seems sufficiently high for it to be acceptable as from Cranach's own hand. It is associated by Friedländer and Rosenberg with a group of similar female portraits from the decade of 1520, and shows clear analogies of handling; they comment that it is doubtful whether such pictures are true portraits or idealized variations by Cranach on a theme.

PROVENANCE: Acquired by the Earl of Shrewsbury from a collection at Nuremberg, very likely that of Friedrich Campe.[1] At Alton Towers by 1835[2]; Earl of Shrewsbury sale, Alton Towers, 8 July (3rd day) 1857 (lot 259), bought for the National Gallery.

REPRODUCTION: *Illustrations, Continental Schools*, 1937, p. 75.

REFERENCES: *General:* Friedländer and Rosenberg, *op. cit.*, no. 147; see also the comment under their no. 150.
In text: (1) The National Gallery MS. Catalogue records the picture as from a collection at Nuremberg. According to Passavant, *Tour of a German Artist in England*, 1836, vol. II, p. 81, two Flemish pictures at Alton Towers had been acquired from the Campe collection and it is likely that No. 291 (not mentioned by Passavant) had the same provenance. It is not among the pictures in *Umrisse zu Oelgemaelden aus der Dr. Fr. Campe'schen Sammlung . . .*, n.d. (2) Waagen, *Treasures of Art in Great Britain*, III, 1854, p. 388; *op. cit.*, p. 381, he notes that his account of the collection dates from 1835. In the 1929 catalogue a further provenance for No. 291 was proposed as the Ottley sale, London, 25 May 1811 (lot 9) Cranach, *Probably a Portrait of a Princess of Saxony*. No. 291 is almost certainly not that picture, in view of the provenance recorded for it.

1925 PORTRAIT OF A MAN

Upper left and right two coats-of-arms, respectively: *Coupé: au 1 d'argent aux trois figues de vert; au 2 de gueules.* And: *De gueules à la*

fasce d'or, accompagné de trois œillets(?) *au naturel.* Signed under the
left-hand shield with the painter's device and dated: *1524.*
Beech, painted area, 16 × 10¼ (0·407 × 0·261).
In quite good condition under discoloured varnish. There is some
cracking and some repaint, most apparent in the face and hands. A
vertical crack left of the sitter.

On the back an inscription in a nineteenth-century hand identifies
the sitter as Franz von Sickingen. Cranach did apparently paint
Sickingen[1] but the sitter in No. 1925 is not he, nor do the coats-of-arms
suggest a member of that family. Franz von Sickingen in any case died
the year before No. 1925 was painted. A further inscription on the back
of the picture, 'H. Doctor | Lüther [*sic*] | 1778', is perhaps the reason why
it was suggested in the 1929 catalogue that the sitter might be a member
of the Luther family. This seems excluded again by the coats-of-arms.
The sitter has some vague resemblance to Hans Luther, father of Martin,
as portrayed by Cranach[2]; perhaps No. 1925 was called Hans or Martin
Luther (though there is no resemblance in this case) in the eighteenth
century.
     The left-hand coat-of-arms is apparently that borne by Johann Feige,
Chancellor of Hesse.[3] Feige (1482(?)–1543) might well have been
painted by Cranach but the sitter of No. 1925 seems too old to be
acceptable as a man of about forty-five.[4] The date on the picture does
not seem to have been tampered with. Perhaps some other, less famous,
member of the Feige family is shown. The present writer has not
succeeded in identifying the coat-of-arms at the right.

PROVENANCE: Said to have been in an anonymous(?) sale, London, (Christie),
1902.[5] Later bought by J. P. Heseltine, by whom presented, 1903.

REPRODUCTION: *Illustrations, Continental Schools,* 1937, p. 75.

REFERENCES: *General:* Friedländer and Rosenberg, no. 153.
     In text: (1) See for instance the picture mentioned by J. Heller, *Das Leben und
die Werke Lucas Cranach's,* 1844 ed., p. 58. A letter of 1934 from E. Mackowsky,
in the Gallery archives, points out that there is no resemblance between the
sitter of No. 1925 and the engraving of Sickingen (after Cranach) published in
the *Reformationsallmanach,* 1819, p. 78. (2) See for instance the picture,
Friedländer and Rosenberg, no. 253; also the drawing reproduced by them,
op. cit., p. 23. (3) Information kindly provided by Dr. H. F. Deininger of the
City Archives, Augsburg. He was not able to identify the other coat-of-arms.
(4) Although Feige's exact date of birth is not established, it is known that he
was studying as a young man at Erfurt *ca.* 1503 and was made chancellor of
Hesse in 1513; cf. the entry by Lenz for him in *Allgemeine Deutsche Biographie,*
VI, 1877. A number of references to him are to be found in *Briefwechsel Land-
graf Philipp's des Grossmüthigen von Hessen mit Bucer* (ed. Lenz) 1880, sqq.
(5) In previous editions of Gallery catalogues, including that of 1929. The
present writer has not succeeded in tracing the sale in question. The provenance
has previously included No. 1925 as in the collection of a Dr. Luther in 1778,
but the inscription on the back hardly establishes this.

2925 CHARITY

A standing woman suckling a child; at the right a boy grasping her leg. At the left a girl holding a doll.

Signed with Cranach's device bottom left. Inscribed in the top left-hand corner: *CHARITAS*

Beech, painted surface, $22\frac{3}{8} \times 14\frac{1}{4}$ (0·563 × 0·362).

In fair condition, but there is considerable wearing and retouching in all the flesh parts.

Friedländer and Rosenberg point out that No. 2925 is likely to be post-1537 owing to the changed form of the snake device, which occurs only from that year onwards.[1] In the 1929 catalogue it was suggested that the picture originated *ca.* 1550 and Cranach's own account of his work at Augsburg (*i.e.* in 1550–1) does mention two pictures of Charity.[2] The subject is quite common in his work, but Charity herself is usually shown seated or lying down; No. 2925 seems unique in this respect and also in the absence of versions. Its condition is a hindrance to attribution, but it may reasonably be accepted as by Cranach and is likely to be late work.

PROVENANCE: Presented by Rosalind, Countess of Carlisle, 1913.

REPRODUCTION: *Illustrations, Continental Schools*, 1937, p. 76.

REFERENCES: *General:* Friedländer and Rosenberg, *op. cit.*, no. 325.
   In text: (1) Friedländer and Rosenberg, *op. cit.*, p. 20. (2) Cf. C. Schuchardt, *Lucas Cranach* . . . , 1851, I, pp. 207–8.

3922 THE CLOSE OF THE SILVER AGE(?)

The subject is discussed in detail below.

Oak, painted surface, $19\frac{3}{4} \times 14\frac{1}{16}$ (0·502 × 0·357).

In general in good condition.

A vaguely similar subject to No. 3922 occurs in a number of pictures by Cranach, each of slightly differing composition, and each was originally supposed to represent no more than a battle of naked men.[1] Later, on analogy with a wrongly interpreted engraving by Dürer, such compositions were said to represent 'The Effects of Jealousy'.[2] Flechsig put forward the suggestion that the subject derived from Hesiod's story of the quarrelsome end to the Silver Age[3] (*Erga*, 132 ff.) and this title has usually been adopted without comment in Cranach literature. More than one edition of Hesiod (*editio princeps*, 1493(?), the *Erga* only) was available for consultation by Cranach and, either directly or indirectly, he seems to have used Hesiod for his painting *The Golden Age*.[4] Flechsig thought Cranach's direct source for the composition as in No. 3922 might be some Latin poem by a contemporary Wittenberg versifier. This is conceivable, for what is shown at any rate in No. 3922 has no real basis in Hesiod's description of the Silver Age.

No. 3922 shows two brown-skinned men, one of whom is hitting a

fallen wounded man while the other stands over a fallen man whom he
has presumably just wounded. In the foreground three women and
three children show varying degrees of interest in the proceedings. All
the figures are naked, which does suggest a classical, or vaguely classical,
scene. There seems to be a contrast intended between the two darker-
skinned victors and the rest of the figures, all of whose skins are noticeably paler.

It would be possible, if Hesiod is in any way the source for the scene,
that Cranach meant to show the coming of the Bronze Age men who
were 'terrible and strong', and perhaps his immediate source (but not
Hesiod) said that they fought the more effete Silver Age men. Just
conceivably the wooden staves in No. 3922, one of which is an uprooted
tree, might be related to a crux in what Hesiod (l. 145) says of the
Bronze Age men, that they were ἐκ μελιᾶν: either 'sprung from ash
trees' or '(terrible) because of their (ashen) spears'.[5]

Flechsig was inclined to ascribe No. 3922 to Hans Cranach; but he
ascribed to this very shadowy personality a number of pictures which
have not won acceptance as such. Hans Cranach's activity as a painter
is definitely established by at least two pictures, one of which, *Hercules
and Omphale*, is signed with the snake device and his initials H.C. and
dated 1537 (the year of his death). It is doubtful if Flechsig knew either
of these pictures; of the *Hercules and Omphale* Friedländer has commented that in the absence of initials the picture would have been
accepted as by the elder Cranach.[6] No. 3922 is accepted as the elder
Cranach's work by Friedländer and Rosenberg. No doubt the studio
were involved in producing the slightly varying designs of this composition (none exactly repeats No. 3922). As mentioned in the biography
above it is very difficult, if not impossible, in the absence of evidence
to separate such work from pictures by Cranach's own hand.[7] It is
perhaps a little unusual that No. 3922 is not signed with the snake
device, but in any case the picture does not seem of such low quality
that studio assistance should be specifically invoked for it, nor would
absence of the device indicate this.

Friedländer and Rosenberg date it *ca.* 1530.[8] Related designs (for
which see under) bear dates 1527, 1529, 1535; all show analogies of
handling and it is reasonable to suppose No. 3922 is of about the same
period.

DRAWING : A silver-point drawing at Berlin, of quite different composition but
vaguely similar subject, is often called (wrongly?) 'The Silver Age'.[9]

VERSIONS : A signed and dated related design (of 1527) is in the Schloss-
museum, Weimar.[10] Another (signed and dated 1529) was in a private collection,
Berlin, in 1932.[11] A third (of 1535) is in the Louvre[12]; a vaguely related picture
was in a private collection, Paris, 1932.[13]

PROVENANCE : By 1880 in the collection of Edward Habich, Cassel, at which
time on loan there with rest of the collection to the Gemäldegalerie (until
1892)[14]; Habich sale, Cassel, 10 May 1892 (lot 86), bought by J. P. Richter for
Dr. Ludwig Mond[15]; Mond bequest, 1924.

REPRODUCTION : *Illustrations, Continental Schools*, 1937, p. 76.

REFERENCES : *General:* Friedländer and Rosenberg, no. 215.
In text: **(1)** See for example J. Heller, *Das Leben und die Werke Lucas Cranach's*, 1844 ed., p. 80. The point is partly taken up again in the catalogue of the exhibition at Weimar and Wittenberg, *Lucas Cranach*, 1953, p. 42 (no. 32). **(2)** Dürer's engraving (Bartsch 73) is actually an allegory of Hercules; for detailed discussion of it see E. Panofsky, *Hercules am Scheidewege*, 1930, pp. 166 ff. **(3)** *Cranachstudien*, 1900, p. 268. **(4)** A composition quite unrelated in size and treatment to the so-called Silver Age pictures; for versions of *The Golden Age*, cf. Friedländer and Rosenberg, nos. 213 and 214. **(5)** For these points further the Loeb Library edition *Hesiod* (ed. H. G. Evelyn-White), 1954, p. 13, may be consulted. **(6)** Thieme-Becker, *Lexikon*, VIII, 1913, under Hans Cranach, with other pertinent comment; see also Friedländer and Rosenberg, *op. cit.*, pp. 19 ff. **(7)** The problem of the Cranach studio is discussed by J. Rosenberg in *The Art Quarterly*, 1955, pp. 165 ff. **(8)** The date is followed by H. Posse, *Lucas Cranach d. Ä.*, 1942, p. 62. **(9)** T. L. Girshausen, *Die Handzeichnungen Lukas Cranachs des Älteren*, n.d. but 1937, p. 74. (no. 56). **(10)** Friedländer and Rosenberg, no. 216; for recent comment see the Weimar exhibition catalogue cited above in the note 1. **(11)** Friedländer and Rosenberg, no. 217. **(12)** Friedländer and Rosenberg, no. 217 (b); in L. Réau, *La Peinture au Musée du Louvre: Ecole Allemande*, 1924, as by Hans Cranach. **(13)** Friedländer and Rosenberg, no. 217 (a). There is a reproduction of the picture in *Les Trésors d'Art en Russie*, 1905, pl. 98, and from this there seems little reason to relate it either to Hesiod or to the 'Silver Age' subject. Other versions (*sic*) of No. 3922 exist; one such is recorded by a letter of 1894 in the Gallery archives as then in the collection of Peter Cooper, London; cf. also further C. Schuchardt, *op. cit.* **(14)** Letter of 1935 from the Gemäldegalerie, Cassel, in the Gallery archives. **(15)** J. P. Richter, *The Mond Collection*, 1910, II, pp. 589–90.

CHRISTIAN WILHELM ERNST DIETRICH

1712–1774

He usually, but not always, signs *Dietricij*.[1] Born at Weimar, 30 October 1712; trained first under his father and *ca.* 1724–5 studying at Dresden under the landscape painter, Alexander Thiele, whom he accompanied to Arnstadt for a stay in 1728. Although settled at Dresden, he spent some years from 1730 onwards either at Weimar or in wanderings through Germany; conceivably he also visited Holland at this period.[2] By 1741 he was back in Dresden where that year he married and was appointed court painter to the Elector Frederick Augustus II of Saxony. In 1743 he travelled in Italy, staying first in Rome, and during the late summer was at Venice.[3] Dietrich retired from Dresden during the Seven Years' War (1756–63), but afterwards returned. He was appointed a professor at Dresden academy in 1764 and died there, 23–4 April 1774.

Dietrich painted nearly every kind of picture, from altarpieces for Saxon churches to small genre scenes. Very early his ability as pasticheur, chiefly of seventeenth-century masters but also of Watteau, was praised and utilized.[4] He practised as etcher and also decorated some Meissen porcelain.[5]

REFERENCES : *General:* C. H. von Heinecken, *Dictionnaire des Artistes . . .* , 1790, IV, pp. 673 ff. Heinecken was well acquainted with Dietrich.
In text: **(1)** The *Adoration of the Kings* (Dresden) signed *C. W. E. Dietrich*

and dated 1731; a *Picture Gallery* (Nuremberg) signed *Ch: Dieterich*, and dated 1742. (2) Heinecken, *op. cit.*, p. 674, says it was in fact in 1734 that the painter visited Holland. (3) Information about his stay there and his proposed journey to Vienna is given in a letter from Francesco Algarotti to Count Brühl, printed by H. Posse in Prussian *Jahrbuch*, 1931, Appendix, p. 57. (4) Cf. the testimony of the painter Georg Weissmann in 1741, letter printed by F. Schlie in *Repertorium für Kunstwissenschaft*, 1886, p. 22. (5) A tankard initialled by him in the Victoria and Albert Museum, London; cf. W. B. Honey in *The Burlington Magazine*, LIX, 1931, pp. 59 ff.

205 THE WANDERING MUSICIANS

In the background at the right an inn with the sign of a jug and compasses.

Signed in the bottom right-hand corner: *Dietricij fecit 1745.*

Oak, $17\frac{1}{16} \times 13$ (0·437 × 0·33).

In very good condition under discoloured varnish.

The composition seems to be derived from an Adriaen van Ostade composition of the same subject,[1] and the style is a pastiche of Ostade's manner. Probably Dietrich knew the original through an engraving of it, in the same direction, by Cornelius Visscher; he has made a few minor alterations and additions, such as the man smoking at the left (though he too is Ostade-inspired) while in the Ostade the foreground man plays a hurdy-gurdy and the boy a fiddle.[2] Dietrich is supposed to have painted more than one version of the subject, with slight changes[3]; certainly he did paint one or two other Ostade pastiches, and he himself etched at a later date the same composition as No. 205.[4]

No. 205 is almost certainly the picture which belonged to Dietrich's friend, the engraver Jean-George Wille (see further under Provenance), whose engraving made the composition famous. Wille's mention of this suggests that it was the first picture Dietrich painted for him.[5] In 1761 he asked Dietrich to paint him a pendant and this pendant, which showed a woman selling pancakes, reached Paris in 1764 and was later engraved by Wille as *Les Offres Réciproques.*[6]

DRAWINGS: A drawing of the complete composition is in the Albertina, Vienna.[7] Another, of the chief part of the composition was in the Bezine sale, Brussels, 14–15 June 1927 (lot 22), signed by Dietrich.[8] A possibly related drawing is at Berlin.[9]

ENGRAVINGS: Engraved in the same direction and same size by J.-G. Wille in 1764.[10] The composition engraved by J. F. Bause in 1777; also engraved by Thomas Cook.

COPIES: A copy is at Stuttgart[11]; another was in an anonymous sale, London, 21 July 1939 (lot 42). A third was at one time in the Wolsey Art Gallery, Ipswich.[12]

PROVENANCE: Almost certainly in the collection of J.-G. Wille, Paris, and by June 1761.[13] Anon. [Wille] sale, Paris, 6 December *sqq.* 1784 (lot 32). In the collection of Richard Simmons by 1836[14]; bequeathed by him, 1846.

REPRODUCTION: *Illustrations, Continental Schools*, 1937, p. 91.

REFERENCES : *General:* The present writer in *Gazette des Beaux-Arts,* 1958, pp. 33 ff.; 'Some paintings by Dietrich for J.-G. Wille'.
In text: (1) It is Hofstede de Groot, No. 433. (2) In a drawing of wandering musicians by Ostade at Berlin the man plays the fiddle as in Dietrich's picture, and there is possibly some influence on No. 205; for the Berlin drawing cf. E. Bock and J. Rosenberg, *Die Niederländischen Meister (Die Zeichnungen alter Meister . . .),* 1931, p. 204 (No. 4050). (3) On this point, compare the comments of Meusel in *Miscellaneen artistischen Inhalts,* V, 1780, p. 49; all the same, there do not seem any versions of No. 205 which could convincingly claim to be by Dietrich himself, and perhaps Meusel had seen some of the copies (compare under this heading) which do exist. (4) C. H. von Heinecken, *Dictionnaire des Artistes . . . ,* 1790, IV, p. 684. (5) *Memoires et Journal de J.-G. Wille* (ed. G. Duplessis), 1857, I, p. 169. The point is further discussed by the present writer as cited above. (6) The last reference to this picture so far traced seems its appearance in the Comte de Pourtalès sale, Paris, 27 March *sqq.* 1865 (lot 149), *la Marchande de gaufres,* the existence of Wille's engraving being noted there. (7) Cf. *Die Zeichnungen der deutschen Schulen,* 1933, p. 124 (no. 1357). There are minor differences between drawing and painting, of which the most obvious is that the listening peasant left has no pipe in the drawing. (8) There is a reproduction in the sale catalogue, plate VI. The text given in the catalogue for what is written on the drawing is wrong; it should read: *C. W. E. Dietricij | Inventor a la Custo di Osta[de?].* The form of the signature is close to that on No. 205, also, for example, on a drawing of 1742 at Dresden. (9) It shows the bust of the fiddler only. (10) Dedicated to the Elector of Saxony; annotated at the lower right: *Gravé en 1764 par J. G. Wille d'après le Tableau | Original de même Grandeur qui lui appartient.* (11) Catalogued as after Wille's engraving; cf. *Katalog der Staatsgalerie . . . ,* 1931, p. 41. (12) Included in the sale of some pictures, etc., from the Gallery, Ipswich, 13 December 1956 (lot 47). (13) Compare the note 5 above. (14) See J. Smith, *Catalogue Raisonné of the works of the most eminent Dutch . . . Painters,* VII, 1836, p. 256.

ALBRECHT DÜRER
1471–1528

His name is variously spelt by contemporaries, *Turer, Thurer,* etc. Born at Nuremberg, 21 May 1471,[1] son of Albrecht Dürer, a goldsmith of Hungarian origin. Trained first as a goldsmith under his father, he was apprenticed on 30 November 1486 to Michael Wohlgemut at Nuremberg for some three years.[2] In 1490 he began his travels[3]; some of the places visited remain conjectural but he was at Colmar in 1492 [4] and probably in the same year also at Bâle.[5] For part of 1493–4 he was apparently active at Strasbourg.[6] He returned to Nuremberg after Whitsun 1494 and was married there on 7 July that year. Apparently later the same year he set out for Italy and was in Venice for part of 1494–5.[7] He visited Italy again in 1505 and was at Venice 1506–7.[8] At Venice he was commissioned to paint the *Rosenkranzfest* (dated 1506; National Gallery, Prague) for S. Bartolommeo, the church of the German merchant colony. He was back in Nuremberg by February 1507. In 1520–1 he made a journey to the Netherlands. The 'Four Apostles' (Munich), which show in their inscriptions Luther's influence on Dürer, were completed and given by the painter to Nuremberg city in 1526.[9] He died at Nuremberg, 6 April 1528.

Dürer's earliest recorded work is a *Self-Portrait* drawing (Vienna) which he later annotated as having done in 1484. The earliest dated painting is the portrait of *Dürer the Elder* (Uffizi, Florence) of 1490. Most of his work is signed and dated, whether etchings, engravings, woodcuts, drawings or paintings. The first published reference to Dürer by a contemporary seems to be that of Jakob Wimpfeling in *Epithoma rerum Germanicarum* . . . , 1505.[10] Apart from treatises on specialized subjects and numerous letters, Dürer also left a 'Family Chronicle' and a diary of his journey to the Netherlands.[11]

REFERENCES: *General:* E. Panofsky, *Albrecht Dürer*, 1945 ed. (2 vols.), F. Winkler, *Albrecht Dürer*, 1957.
In text: (1) The date is from Dürer's *Familienchronik* which was compiled in part from his father's papers; the original manuscript is lost. The latest careful publication, and discussion, is in *Dürer. Schriftlicher Nachlass* (ed. H. Rupprich) I, 1956, pp. 27 ff. (2) *Familienchronik, ed. cit.*, p. 31. Dürer's exact words are 'drei jahr lang jhm zu dienen'. (3) For discussion of these years, see especially E. Roemer in Prussian *Jahrbuch*, 1926, pp. 118 ff.; and the same writer, *loc. cit.*, 1927, pp. 77 ff. and pp. 156 ff. (4) Where he was in touch with the brothers of Schongauer (*q.v.*). The fact is given by Christoph Scheurl, *Vita reverendi patris domini Anthonii Kressen*, 1515; passage reprinted in Rupprich, *op. cit.*, p. 294. (5) Scheurl, *loc. cit.* The artistic evidence is a woodcut of S. Jerome, title page of *Epistolare beati Hieronymi* published at Bâle, 1492; see the discussion in Panofsky, *op. cit.*, II, p. 49 (no. 414). (6) There are two woodcuts (Panofsky, *op. cit.* II, pp. 55–6, nos. 441–2), usually attributed to Dürer, in the *Opus Speciale Missarum*, published at Strasbourg, 1493. Willibald Imhoff the Elder's inventory of his collection (1573–4) records a pair of portraits which seem to have been painted by Dürer at Strasbourg; see further Rupprich, *op. cit.*, p. 34, note 49. (7) The evidence is small but definite; apart from drawings and watercolours, it rests on Dürer's letter from Venice to Pirckheimer, of 7 February 1506, in which he speaks of being no longer pleased by what had pleased him there eleven years before. (8) Dürer's letters from Venice to Pirckheimer, Rupprich, *op. cit.*, pp. 39 ff., provide the most useful evidence. For a general guide to Dürer's Venetian stays, cf. L. Grote, '*Hier ich bin ein Herr*': *Dürer in Venedig*, 1956. (9) See Dürer's letter of 6 October 1526 to the City Council: Rupprich, *op. cit.*, pp. 117 ff. (10) The text in Rupprich, *op. cit.*, p. 290. (11) The latest edition of the writings is Rupprich, *op. cit.*, 1956 ff., which includes the documents on and related to Dürer; the latter have never otherwise been assembled by Dürer scholarship. For the Netherlandish Journey, see also the elaborate edition of J. Veth and S. Muller, *Albrecht Dürers niederländische Reise*, 1918 (2 vols.).

Ascribed to DÜRER

1938 THE PAINTER'S FATHER

Inscribed at the top: *1497 · ALBRECHT · THVRER · DER · ELTER · VND · ALT · 70 IOR*. Bottom right-hand corner (an old inventory number?): *208*.

Lime, painted area, $20\frac{1}{16} \times 15\frac{7}{8}$ (0·51 × 0·397).

The condition is not very good, but since cleaning it is apparent that the picture is by no means a wreck. In general there is not a great deal of wearing but there is considerable cracking, especially in the background, the fur, tunic, and in parts of the robe. The cracking of the paint is apparently due to a flaw in the original technique. The face and hair are in quite good state and most of the quality of the picture seems not to have been affected. There is a minor *pentimento* in the outline of the cap and another in the contour of the robe at the right. Cleaned in 1955.

Albrecht Dürer the Elder was born at Ajtas in Hungary, 1427, and the surname is supposedly derived from this place ('Ajtas' meaning door, so *Tür* or *Dür* in German).[1] He settled in Nuremberg in 1455 and practised as a goldsmith.[2] He married Barbara Holper in 1467 and died at Nuremberg in 1502.

No. 1938 was acquired as by Dürer; but a number of critics at the time, of whom the most important was Campbell Dodgson, expressed doubts about the attribution.[3] It is in the 1929 catalogue as by Dürer. The picture is likely to have been one of a pair of portraits presented by the city of Nuremberg to Charles I, through the Earl of Arundel, in 1636. The two pictures were not, however, pendants. The other portrait was of Dürer himself, and is the picture signed and dated 1498 now in the Prado, Madrid.[4]

Both pictures were in the city's possession by 1627. It is not known how they had been acquired, but they were clearly valued at Nuremberg as originals by Dürer.[5] This does not of course establish the authenticity of No. 1938, although the picture is, as Panofsky has indicated, apparently the most adequate surviving replica of the design[6] (see further under Versions and Copies). Panofsky does not accept it as Dürer's original and the tendency of most scholars has been to reject it. It is not accepted by Friedländer,[7] by the Tietzes,[8] nor by Flechsig.[9] Buchner expresses reservations about it.[10] But for one or two scholars, of whom Winkler is the chief, the quality and technique are such as to make it acceptably by Dürer.[11] Dr. Winkler has kindly written to the present writer with his latest views on the picture (which he has studied in photographs since cleaning). He still finds a close relationship between No. 1938 and the Uffizi portrait of the elder Dürer (dated 1490) in drawing and modelling, and for him the only surprising element is the pink background virtually revealed by cleaning.[12]

It seems reasonable to accept that the composition of No. 1938, along with its inscription, in effect records a portrait by Dürer of his father painted in 1497, even if No. 1938 is not the original. The only other acceptable explanation would be that the painted versions all derive from a lost drawing of 1497 by Dürer. If No. 1938 is an original painting of 1497 by Dürer it should be closely related not only to the Uffizi portrait but also to other portraits by Dürer of the same decade: the Louvre *Self-Portrait* (1493), the Prado *Self-Portrait* (1498), the Munich *Oswolt Krel* (1499). For the present writer these three pictures, and the Uffizi portrait, form a stylistic group into which No. 1938 does not fit. Comparison with the Prado *Self-Portrait* is particularly relevant, for not only is that picture of only one year later than No. 1938 (granting this to be by Dürer) but it is established as having belonged to Charles I. Examination of the two pictures within a brief space of time has convinced the present writer that the whole technique of the two pictures is strikingly different.

It may be objected that the quality of No. 1938 is too high for it to be merely a copy, but on the other hand it can hardly be denied that it shows marked divergences from other portraits by Dürer of the same decade. (Its quality, one may note in passing, seemed to Roger Fry to indicate that it was indeed no more than a copy.[13]) The drawing of the robe and hand is unusually clumsy, as are the shadows on the face and neck. The scratchy technique of the eyes is noticeably unlike the treatment of them in any of the portraits already mentioned—or indeed in any other portraits by Dürer. These divergences cannot be explained by immaturity, and the present writer cannot explain them except by supposing No. 1938 to be by a hand not Dürer's own. Even allowing the utmost for deterioration arising from technique (and that deterioration is itself so unusual in Dürer as to amount to another argument for rejection), grounds for doubt seem justified. Technical examination does not support a suggestion that the picture is unfinished, and the inscription is also evidence against that.

The inscription of No. 1938 is puzzling. Tests carried out at the time of cleaning showed convincingly that this had been painted directly on to the pink background.[14] The likelihood is that the inscription is very little later, if at all, than the picture. No critic seems to have proposed that the actual painting of the inscription on No. 1938 was done by Dürer himself, though the phrasing of it might be derived from him.[15] Certainly the lettering is quite unlike the lettering placed by Dürer on other pictures.

One version of the design (that at the time of writing at Bamberg), admittedly not by Dürer, is inscribed differently and the inscription is placed alongside the sitter: *1497 | Das malt Ich nach meines vatters* [sic] *gestalt | Da Er war sibenzich Jar alt | Albrecht Dürer Der elter.* Dürer's monogram is below. This inscription is such a clear echo of the inscription on the Madrid *Self-Portrait*, which it resembles in handwriting, that either it is a deliberate copy or it records the original form of an inscription on the original portrait of 1497 of Dürer the elder. Before the discovery of No. 1938, the second possibility was considered and accepted by Friedländer[16] and for a time by Dodgson.[17]

Leaving aside this question, if the inscription of No. 1938 is not by Dürer but the picture is his, then it is unusual in his *œuvre* in having been left uninscribed by him, unsigned and, more important perhaps, undated. What is even more unusual is that no forged monogram or date was later supplied; their absence suggests that the present inscription on No. 1938 was already there and did duty for them. Yet the inscription does not claim that Dürer painted the picture, though perhaps that point should not be pressed.

The provenance of No. 1938 is vexed chiefly because there is a gap of more than two hundred years between its presumed presence in

Charles I's collection and its definite presence in the collection of
Louisa, Lady Ashburton, ca. 1900. The evidence for supposing that the
Charles I picture was similar in design to No. 1938 is very strong. The
composition accords with Vanderdoort's description, while his specific
mention of the 'reddish ground all crackt' would seem to indicate No.
1938 in particular. The other copies, or versions, do not have any effect
of cracking and the ground is yellowish brown or grey rather than red.
Hollar engraved in 1644 a design similar to that of No. 1938 but that
differs in the detailed formation of the letters of the inscription.[18]
Hollar does not state the whereabouts of the picture in question. He also
engraved the Dürer Self-Portrait (Prado design), in 1645, and that
engraving bears the words 'ex Collectione Arundeliana'. But the
original did not of course belong to Arundel, though Arundel apparently
owned a copy of it; in which case, it would be possible that he also
owned a copy of Dürer the Elder.[19]

In fact, Arundel is known to have commissioned copies of both
pictures from a certain Greenbury. It has not previously been published
that these were bought by the king and were intended to be sent to
Nuremberg in reciprocation for the originals.[20] There is no evidence
that they were ever sent and no record of their receipt at Nuremberg.[21]
It is quite likely that the copies remained in store and the outbreak of the
Civil War finally prevented their despatch.[22]

An objection to accepting No. 1938 as the Charles I picture may seem
to be that, unlike the majority of the king's collection, it is not stamped
or branded on the back. But neither is the Dürer Self-Portrait (Prado),
the provenance of which from Charles I is established; that picture
appears to have been painted on the back, as does No. 1938, and it also
bears an original damaged label dating from the time of its presence in
Charles I's collection.[23] No. 1938 bears no label, but this could easily
have been obliterated in its wanderings. All that can be said is that the
absence of royal stamp or brand from its back does not invalidate the
supposition that it belonged to the king.

The present writer thinks the picture is very likely to be that given by
the city of Nuremberg to Charles I, and accepted in good faith by both
parties as a Dürer. Nevertheless, it has not won general acceptance as
Dürer's original, and the doubts expressed about it seem justified. Since,
however, it cannot be proved to be a copy, and since some reputable
scholars still hold it to be an original, it is catalogued as above.

VERSIONS AND COPIES : A copy (at the time of writing at Bamberg) with a
different form of inscription, belongs to the Bayerisches Staatsgemäldesamm-
lungen and has been referred to above.[24] Another, inscribed as No. 1938 but
dated 1494, is at Frankfurt.[25] Apparently a third is recorded in the Brabeck
collection, Söder, by 1814: in the Count Andreas von Stolberg sale, Hanover,
31 October sqq. 1859 (lot 80). This picture, or perhaps another, belonged later
to the Skorzewski family and was once on loan to Posen.[26] A version in the Duke
of Northumberland's collection, at Syon House, has been claimed as by Greenbury (whose copies have been mentioned above).[27] A doubtfully old copy
following No. 1938 closely is in the collection of Mrs. Davies, Camberley. The
design apparently influenced Jacopo de' Barbari's S. Oswald (of 1500).[28]

ENGRAVINGS: The design (without any inscription) engraved in reverse by an unknown German (?) author, undated.[29] The design engraved in reverse (with inscription) by Hollar, print dated 1644. A derivative, probably from one of these, uninscribed, bust length in their direction, engraved in Sandrart.[30]

PROVENANCE: Probably the picture presented with Dürer's *Self-Portrait* (of 1498) by the City of Nuremberg to Charles I, through the Earl of Arundel, in November 1636.[31] That picture is recorded as in the city's possession by August, 1627.[32] The pair of pictures received by the king by 18 March 1637.[33] In Vanderdoort's catalogue of Charles I collection, 1639, as at Whitehall.[34] Charles I sale, July 1650.[35] Seen afterwards by Richard Symonds, with the *Self-Portrait*, at 'Mr. Knightleyes' (*sic*), *ca.* 1652.[36] Claimed wrongly in an inventory of Restoration date to have been returned to the Royal Collection, with the Prado *Self Portrait*.[37] At a later date No. 1938 was probably still in England.[38] No. 1938 owned by Louisa, Lady Ashburton (†1903). Inherited by the Marquess of Northampton; exhibited at the Royal Academy, 1904 (no. 10). Bought from the Marquess of Northampton, 1904.

REPRODUCTION: *Illustrations, Continental Schools*, 1937, p. 96.

REFERENCES: (1) See E. Panofsky, *Albrecht Dürer*, 1945 ed., I, p. 4. (2) The date is from the Dürer *Familienchronik*, but the first reference to him in Nuremberg is apparently of 1444; for this and his biography in general, cf. A. Gümbel in *Repertorium für Kunstwissenschaft*, 1915, pp. 210 ff. (3) See first Dodgson's article in *The Athenæum*, 1904, p. 185, a résumé of his notes (with S. M. Peartree) for *The Dürer Society*, 1901, pp. 7 ff., and *loc. cit.*, 1902, p. 4. At the time of that being written, the inscription on No. 1938 was not visible (being hidden by the frame) nor had the picture been bought by the National Gallery. Dodgson's résumé there admirably states the whole question about No. 1938 and the other versions, apart from minor points which have since come to light. See also C. J. Holmes in *The Burlington Magazine*, V, 1904, pp. 431 ff., where the picture is claimed as a Dürer; and further *loc. cit.*, pp. 570 ff., for various contributions (of various merit) on the subject. (4) *Museo del Prado: Catalogo* ..., 1949, pp. 171–2. Some further information about this picture is given in the penultimate paragraph of text above. (5) Thus when the Elector of Bavaria was attempting in 1627 to acquire the 'Four Apostles', among the reasons given to the city council by their adviser that they might yield, was that the city still owned 'einiger Dürer'scher Kunstwerke z. B. des Bildnisses von Dürer und dessen Vater ...'; cf. J. Baader, *Beiträge zur Kunstgeschichte Nürnbergs*, 1860, p. 13. (6) Panofsky, *op. cit.*, II, no. 53 (p. 14). (7) *Albrecht Dürer*, 1921, p. 69. (8) H. Tietze and E. Tietze-Conrat, *Kritisches Verzeichnis der Werke Albrecht Dürers*, vol. I, 1928, p. 89 (W. 12). (9) E. Flechsig, *Albrecht Dürer*, I, 1928, pp. 358 ff., with exhaustive but not always accurate discussion of the problem. See also H. Tietze in *Wiener Jahrbuch für Kunstgeschichte*, 1930, p. 241, and C. S. Zilva in *Apollo*, 1935, p. 238. (10) E. Buchner, *Das deutsche Bildnis der Spätgotik und der frühen Dürerzeit*, 1953, p. 150. (11) According to the comments of S. M. P(eartree) in *The Dürer Society* (8th series), 1905, p. 4, note 1, Bayersdorfer expressed belief in No. 1938 as by Dürer. *The Dürer Society* (*Index . . . Portfolios I–X, 1898–1908*), 1911, p. 67, records that Weixlgärtner had cautiously stated that in reproduction the picture made a favourable impression on him. Winkler's ed. of Klassiker der Kunst *Dürer, n.d.,* p. 3, reproduces No. 1938 as the original; see his text *op. cit.,* pp. 407–8; also his review of the Tietzes, *op. cit.* in *Cicerone*, 1928, p. 471. (12) Letter of 1957 in the Gallery archives. (13) *The Burlington Magazine*, V, 1904, p. 572. (14) A brownish glaze, which tests showed to be not original, did not come between the background and the inscription, but covered them both; see further the note on this point by Joyce Plesters in *Studies in Conservation*, II, 1956, no. 3, p. 7. (15) It does not seem a very strong objection to the inscription's authenticity that the name is given as 'Thurer'. Flechsig, *loc. cit.*, attaches importance to the spelling of the name in No. 1938 to show that the inscription is not derived from one by Dürer himself.

In view of the divergences of spelling of the name which occur at the time—
Dürer's own friends often spell his name with a T— this is perhaps too large an
assumption. **(16)** See his article in *Repertorium für Kunstwissenschaft*, 1896, pp.
12 ff. Rhyming inscriptions of this kind are quite common on portraits of the
period and later. **(17)** That is, at the time of his *Athenæum* article, for which see
the note 3. **(18)** The inscription on Hollar's engraving makes the same mistake
as does the inscription on the Syon version (see Versions and Copies), *i.e.*
putting *VI ID* for *VND*. The mistake seems to arise from the faintness of the
cross stroke of the *N* in No. 1938, which might be proof that the Syon picture is
copied from No. 1938. It does not prove that Hollar engraved from the Syon
picture, nor even that he engraved from some other copy. If the person who
painted the Syon picture could misread the *VND* of No. 1938, Hollar could do
so as well; conceivably, therefore, his engraving derives from No. 1938. **(19)**
The whole matter is confused by the fact that the copies were seldom recognized
as such. The Arundel inventory of 1655 lists a *Portrait of Albert Durer* (no. 110),
but does not mention any portrait of Dürer the elder; cf. Mary F. S. Hervey,
The Life . . . of Thomas Howard, Earl of Arundel, 1921, p. 478. See also the note
20 below. **(20)** Attention was very kindly drawn to this fact by Oliver Millar
who placed at the present writer's disposal his transcripts of the relevant MS.
quoted below. MS. Ashmole, 1514 (of pictures kept in store and as yet unplaced)
folio 161: 'Item, two coppies of Alberdure and his ffather which are done by
Mr. Greenburie by the appoyntment of the Lord Marshall' (*i.e.* Arundel).
Added in another hand, probably Vanderdoort's: *vor tŭ bi sent tŭ norembrek in
rackempenz aŭfft prinsipals*, and further in the same hand (?): *baeht bÿ ta king*.
In the margin 'Coppied by Mr. Greenburye' seems merely a gloss. The painter
is presumably Richard Greenbury (died *ca.* 1670?) for whom there is an entry
in Thieme-Becker *Lexikon*, XIV, p. 570. **(21)** Dr. Hirschmann of the Staatsarchiv at Nuremberg has very kindly checked for the present writer the letter-
books of the Council at the relevant period. Nothing is recorded there of any
correspondence between Charles I and the Council, except for one exchange of
letters in 1641 entirely concerned with political matters. **(22)** It would be
possible that these two copies were dispersed, one into the Arundel collection
(*i.e.* the *Self-Portrait* later recorded there, and engraved as there by Hollar) and
the other into the Northumberland collection (*i.e.* the copy of No. 1938 now at
Syon). **(23)** A fact not previously recorded. The back has been examined by
Oliver Millar and the label is transcribed here from the text he has kindly
supplied: '*to the Kinge | of Nere . . . e brought by | the E. rle . . . Arundell
Ear . . . | Marshall KG, Ambasso . . . | Extraordinary to the Emp . . . | 1636*'.
(24) It is reproduced in V. Scherer, *Klassiker der Kunst Dürer*, 1904, p. 5.
There can be no doubt that this picture is a copy and it seems to the present
writer inferior to the Syon version. The size is approximately that of No. 1938.
It is hard to believe that it copies No. 1938, for the background is a yellowish
brown (clearly the original colour) quite unlike the background of the picture
recorded by Vanderdoort and that of No. 1938 before and after cleaning. The
difference between the background of No. 1938 and the other versions [*sic*] is
obscured by Holmes' remarks, *loc. cit.* on the supposed retouchings making No.
1938 redder; since cleaning it is seen that No. 1938's background is even less
like that of the known copies. **(25)** Size 0·59 × 0·43. The date is simply a copyist's
mistake from the form of the 7 on the original; see the discussion in H. Weizsäcker's Frankfort catalogue, 1900, pp. 94–5. The greyish background is apparently quite unrelated to that of No. 1938, but the picture has not been seen
by the present writer. **(26)** A replica or old copy, taken back by the owners in
1936 and present whereabouts (if it has survived) unknown. The Posen Museum
negative of the picture was destroyed during the 1939–45 war. These comments
kindly supplied by P. Michalowski in a letter of 1958 in the Gallery archives.
(27) The Syon picture must presumably be accepted as a copy, but its quality
seems to the present writer higher than that of such other copies after (?) No.
1938 as he knows. The size is approximately that of No. 1938 but the brownish
background again shows no correspondence; the picture has recently been

cleaned. The inscription follows that on No. 1938 except for the difference
discussed in the note 18 above. (28) Commented on by Panofsky, *op. cit.* I, p. 41.
(29) A print in the British Museum. It bears upper right: *Obijt 1502 | Ætat.
75. | AD.* (usual monogram); beneath the portrait a quatrain celebrating Dürer
the elder and his son 'der solche Stück gemahlt'. (30) *Die Teutscher Akademie*,
1675 ed., II Theil, opp. p. 124. (31) Referred to by William Crowne, *A True
'Relation . . . of all the Remarkable Places and Passages observed in the Travels
of . . . the Earl of Arundell and Surrey*, 1637, p. 56. Arundel's embassy with
regard to Nuremberg discussed in detail by A. Gümbel in *Archivalische Zeitschrift*, 1904, pp. 100 ff.; an extract from the letter of 14 November 1636,
presented with the pictures, given by C. Dodgson in *The Burlington Magazine*,
V, 1904, p. 570. (32) See the note 5 here, referring to J. Baader, *Beiträge zur
Kunstgeschichte Nürnbergs*, 1860, p. 13. (33) This letter is in the Staatsarchiv,
Nuremberg, and is actually dated 18 March 1636 'regnique nostri xii'; the
present writer has consulted it through the kindness of Dr. Hirschmann.
Baader, *op. cit.*, p. 14, noted the exact date of the letter and therefore supposed
the pictures to have been given to Charles (by a slip, he says Charles II) in 1635.
Gümbel, *op. cit.*, p. 115, note 2, thought the date of the letter, which was then
mislaid, had been wrongly quoted by Baader and corrected it to 1637. The
original letter is annotated as read at Nuremberg, 20 April 1637, so the latter
must be the year in which the king wrote—however the date on the letter is to
be explained. (34) In Vertue's publication of Vanderdoort's *Catalogue*, 1757,
p. 157 (no. 26). (35) Among the pictures on exhibition for sale at Somerset
House, with the *Self-Portrait*; cf. the document published by G. J. de Cosnac,
Les Richesses de Palais Mazarin, 1885, p. 416, nos. 64–5. (36) See G. Redford,
Art Sales, 1888, I, p. 17. The quotation above from MS. Egerton 1636, folio
97. (37) B.M. Add. MS. 17916 (Colonel Hawley's list of pictures recovered
for Charles II), folio 9 v: 'Alberdues ffather and himself both of his own doeing'.
The reference kindly supplied by Oliver Millar who has noted other instances of
this error, no doubt through the copying-in of entries from an earlier inventory.
The *Self-Portrait* had then already been acquired by the Spanish ambassador
for the Spanish royal collections. (38) A much damaged label on the back of
No. 1938, inscribed in an eighteenth century(?) hand: 'his profession | . . .
daughter | married . . .'. This is probably a note on the elder Dürer who
married the daughter of the goldsmith who was his master.

Style of DÜRER

5592 THE VIRGIN AND CHILD ('THE MADONNA WITH THE IRIS')

In the sky above the Virgin's head, God the Father.
Falsely monogrammed and almost certainly falsely dated: *1508*.
Lime, painted surface, $58\frac{3}{4} \times 46\frac{1}{8}$ (1·492 × 1·172).
In general in fair but uneven condition, being rather worn and in
parts repainted. The Virgin's face, and most of the flesh areas, have
suffered considerably. Her veil is likely to be a later addition. Her dress
is not repainted but her cloak is in parts very considerably repainted,
more particularly at the right where areas of it are damaged. Most of the
plants are in good condition. There is a *pentimento*, revealed by infra-red
photography, of a rosebud with stem and leaves in the wall right of the
Virgin's head. Cleaned in 1945, before acquisition by the Gallery.[1]

The subject is basically that of the Virgin and Child in the *Hortus
conclusus*, but there are unusual features such as the ruined arch at the

left[2] and the sea beyond. It is perhaps as well to remark on the un-usualness of these, since many other unusual points arise in discussing No. 5592. The significance of some of the plants, notably the iris, has been commented upon by Panofsky among others; as, probably, a symbol of the sword of the Seven Dolours of the Virgin, the iris frequently appears in Northern pictures.[3] The species in No. 5592 has been identified as iris *trojana*.[4]

The group of the Virgin suckling the Child is clearly related to treatments of the theme by Dürer in drawings and engravings, and the conception of them seated on a grassy bank also occurs frequently in his work.[5] The appearance of God the Father in the sky can be paralleled by his rather similar appearances in some of those Dürer compositions, though he is never shown there on such a minute scale.[6] There are some plant studies by Dürer which seem to have formed the basis for some of the plants in No. 5592.[7] Indeed, the picture is almost suspiciously full of Dürer motifs and, as the Tietzes among others have emphasized, these do not seem very intelligently treated.[8] Motifs from Dürer in the picture also range over a surprisingly wide period; thus the Virgin and Child group seems related not only to a woodcut (Bartsch 44) which is almost certainly earlier than the date on No. 5592 but also to a drawing which is dated 1512.[9] At the same time there are elements, like the arch and sea beyond it, which have no real basis in Dürer's work.[10]

The monogram and date on No. 5592 have been the subject of some critical discussion. Few scholars have been prepared to accept the date of 1508 without either elaborate hypotheses or considerable caution.[11] Flechsig's suggestion,[12] that the last digit was a 3 which had been altered, is not tenable but at least pays tribute to the uneasiness pro-voked by the picture which in general treatment suggests Dürer's manner at a period well before 1508.

Examination of the picture shows that the monogram is merely a feeble copy of Dürer's monogram. The picture shows no trace of ever having been signed by Dürer. Recent tests on the paint of the date have shown that the first digit of the 1508 is false, being in quite different paint from that on the rest of the picture. The remaining digits are certainly repainted similarly but show traces of some earlier paint underneath. The traces are very slight and are anyway probably not as old as the picture; this paint appears again on the Virgin's clumsy veil which looks like a later addition. The evidence is not quite conclusive about the date on No. 5592 but suggests strongly that the picture originally bore no date. Two similar compositions, usually accepted as copies derived from No. 5592, significantly lack dates (and monograms) and this would support the probability that No. 5592 was not originally dated. In these circumstances there would be no need to suggest that Dürer added the date when completing the picture after a considerable interval of time. In any case, Dürer did not sign the picture; and the date at which it was painted seems in need of being established.

The question of date is linked to a proposed identification of No. 5592 with a *Maria bildt* offered by Dürer to Jacob Heller in August 1508

and which Heller had seen at Nuremberg in the summer of 1507.[13] The
suggestion that Dürer referred to the composition of No. 5592 was
apparently made first by Thausing (in connection with a copy at
Prague).[14] It has been taken up in connection with No. 5592 by a
number of writers, being first proposed by Dodgson.[15] It was accepted
by the Tietzes[16] and is cautiously accepted by Panofsky.[17] The argument would run that Dürer, and/or his studio, had begun the picture
some time earlier but that it was not signed and dated, perhaps too was
not finished, until the time it was offered by Dürer to Heller. The *Maria
bildt* in question was soon after sold by Dürer to the Bishop of Breslau
for 72 florins, and the painter considered he had sold it well. He had
earlier told Heller he would take 30 or even 25 florins for it: a price
which has suggested to some scholars that he acknowledged the picture
as only a studio piece.[18]

It has already been pointed out that the grounds for associating No.
5592 with the year 1508 are weak—at best. There are further considerable objections to supposing No. 5592 to be the picture to which Dürer
was referring as the *Maria bildt* for sale in 1508. Dürer's letters to Heller
tend to exaggeration in tone, as painters' letters to their patrons often do.
Panofsky has already commented on some of the exaggerated statements
in these letters.[19] When speaking of the *Maria bildt* Dürer says he would
not take less than 50 florins to paint one like it (letter of 24 August
1508).[20] That seems a very low hypothetical price to quote for a picture
as large and elaborate as No. 5592, and no amount of studio intervention
could alter the size or the great detail of the picture.

Such a picture is in fact too large to have been painted as a speculation
and if Heller saw it at Nuremberg in 1507 it is odd that Dürer did not
explain to him how it had become available by 1508 for anyone to buy.
What is more striking is that Dürer told Heller that he had sold his
Maria bildt well for 72 florins (letter of 4 November 1508)[21] but by 1509
was telling Heller that he had refused a commission to paint a Madonna
in a landscape for which he had been offered 400 florins (letter of 26
August 1509)[22]—a picture intended to be almost the same size as No.
5592. Not only is there an obvious discrepancy between the sums
quoted, but it would be very remarkable that Dürer in telling Heller
did not lament selling No. 5592 for so cheap a price when he was afterwards offered nearly six times that amount to paint what would be
virtually the same picture. Especially, it may be added, as the Bishop of
Breslau did not pay until two years later.[23]

To the present writer the inferences are that the *Maria bildt* bought
by the Bishop of Breslau was a small picture; and that it was probably a
Maria bildt without a landscape. Whatever that picture was, there are
no grounds for linking it with No. 5592 and the attempts to do so remain
unconvincing.

No other identification for No. 5592 has been proposed and thus the
picture is strangely unrecorded in Dürer's lifetime and after. As can be
seen below, its provenance does not take it back before 1800. Yet, if it
is by Dürer it surely originated as a commission, and fairly surely as an

altarpiece; it would then be unique among the small group of his large, important, religious pictures in being unsigned, undated, undocumented and unrecorded.

The highest claimed for the picture is that it is the product of collaboration between Dürer and his assistants. This view was advanced by Dodgson who was perhaps the chief champion of No. 5592 as in effect by Dürer.[24] It is supported by Flechsig.[25] The picture is accepted as a workshop production by the Tietzes.[26] By Panofsky it is said to be 'probably the original' of the composition, but he accepts workshop participation.[27] The possible intervention of the studio has led some critics to suggest that Baldung's hand is on No. 5592. This theory was first put forward by Sir Claude Phillips,[28] and was echoed by Charles Ricketts.[29] Some passages in the picture, particularly the treatment of the flesh, do have an affinity with Baldung's manner: the Virgin's hair too might be claimed as reminiscent of Baldung. However, Baldung's presence in Dürer's studio is not a fact but a supposition and, moreover, the present writer is not convinced that the handling of any part of No. 5592 is actually by Baldung.[30]

One group of scholars has not accepted No. 5592 as originating in Dürer's studio at any date. Friedländer called it the work of an imitator[31] and Glück, discussing the picture in more detail, suggested that it might be a product of the late sixteenth-century 'Dürer-Renaissance', done at the court of Rudolph II.[32] In this connection he showed how early copies and pastiches of Dürer, done at Prague, were being accepted as by Dürer himself. Winkler has shared Glück's opinion that No. 5592 is an early forgery rather than the copy of a lost original.[33] Dr. Winkler has very kindly drawn up for the present writer his conclusions against the authenticity of No. 5592, and these are summarized here. He rejects the monogram and date (an opinion confirmed by what has been reported above), finds the style of various parts of the picture of conflicting periods, and in places, especially the vine and peony, unlike Dürer and seemingly of later date. He believes the composition to be in general the invention of an unknown painter, using Dürer motifs and drawings; and points out that the three closest drawings, including that of the iris, were in the collection of Rudolph II by the end of the sixteenth century.

The present writer feels that these points, in conjunction with what has already been said, make it doubtful if No. 5592 can any longer be accepted as a Dürer (with or without studio participation). It is impossible to accept most of the handling as his, while the composition itself seems too weak for him. The provenance is virtually non-existent. There is no signature, and almost certainly no date; and no very acceptable period within Dürer's œuvre for the picture's execution.

But it is as yet very far from established that No. 5592 is a deliberate forgery. It may be said rather that the apparently later addition of signature and date is evidence against that view. Perhaps also the pentimento of the rosebud is a slight but further piece of evidence against supposing the picture to be a forgery. Few if any of the 'Dürer-

Renaissance' pictures are more than copies (often copies after engravings); conflation of Dürer motifs, combined with invention on the scale of No. 5592, is most unusual. It seems to the present writer rather more likely that No. 5592 was painted in Dürer's style but not originally intended to pass as a Dürer. The picture is obviously old and arguably near to Dürer's lifetime or a little after. The technique offers no grounds for specifically putting the picture outside the sixteenth century.

COPIES: A copy is in the National Gallery at Prague [34]; another, apparently smaller, in in the Benedictine monastery of Wilhering, near Linz. [35]

PROVENANCE: Said to have been at some time pre-1821 at Nuremberg. [36] By 1821 at Vienna in the Felsenberg collection. [37] Acquired thence by P. H. Desvignes, by whom brought to England when he settled here. [38] Offered by him in 1872 to the National Gallery. [39] Apparently sold by the son of P. H. Desvignes in 1891. [40] Acquired in 1892 by Sir Francis Cook. Exhibited at the Royal Academy, 1902 (no. 3), lent by Sir Frederick Cook; Burlington Fine Arts Club, 1906 (no. 36). Bought from the Trustees of the Cook collection, through the National Art-Collections Fund, 1945; National Art-Collections Fund exhibition, 1946 (no. 21).

REPRODUCTIONS: Cook collection, *Doughty House Catalogue*, III, 1915, facing p. 108. *The Burlington Magazine*, LXXXVI–LXXXVII, 1945, p. 272 (after cleaning).

REFERENCES: *General*: C. Dodgson in *The Burlington Magazine*, LXXXVI–LXXXVII, 1945, pp. 273 ff.
　　In text: (1) A note, chiefly on the cleaning, by S. C. Kaines-Smith in *The Connoisseur* (116), 1945, pp. 71 ff. (2) According to M. W. Brockwell in the Cook collection, Doughty House catalogue, III, 1915, p. 108, the broken arch is symbolic of the downfall of paganism at the birth of Christ. (3) Cf. E. Panofsky, *Albrecht Dürer*, 1945 ed., vol. II, p. 10 (no. 28); compare also the same author's comments in *Early Netherlandish Painting*, 1953, vol. I, p. 141. (4) On this point see K. Romney Towndrow in *The Burlington Magazine*, LXXXIX, 1947, p. 392; it has not, however, any real bearing on the date of execution of No. 5592. (5) See especially the detailed discussions in H. Tietze and E. Tietze-Conrat, *Kritisches Verzeichnis der Werke Albrecht Dürers*, vol. II, 1937, pp. 145 ff. and Panofsky, *op. cit.*, 1945, II, under his no. 28 (p. 10); also Dodgson cited in the general reference above. (6) It seems a further slight oddity in No. 5592 that the Dove does not appear with God the Father; Dürer usually includes both Persons in such depictions. (7) The most direct instance in No. 5592 is in the iris. This is derived, with slight variations, from a drawing at Bremen: F. Lippmann—F. Winkler, *Zeichnungen von Albrecht Dürer*, VI, 1927, no. 637 (facsimile reproduction); F. Winkler, *Die Zeichnungen Albrecht Dürers*, II, 1937, no. 347, and pp. 68–9. It is falsely dated 1508. Winkler, *loc. cit.*, dates it around 1495; Panofsky, *op. cit.*, II, no. 1430, as about 1503. It would be difficult not to recognize the weaker treatment of the plant in No. 5592 when compared with the drawing. (8) See their discussion, *loc. cit.* (9) A drawing of the Madonna suckling the Child (Vienna) in which the Child's pose is closely akin to that in No. 5592: Lippmann, *op. cit.*, no. 525; Winkler, *op. cit.*, no. 512. This drawing was copied in a painting by Daniel Fröschel, also at Vienna; cf. the reproductions by G. Glück in Vienna *Jahrbuch*, 1909–10, pls. IV and V. (10) Despite the attempts of E. Flechsig, *Albrecht Dürer*, 1928, I, p. 397, to find some parallels. (11) In addition to literature already cited, cf. E. Heidrich, *Geschichte des Dürerschen Marienbildes*, 1906, pp. 185–6. (12) Flechsig, *op. cit.*, pp. 399–400. His positive feeling that the picture cannot be of 1508 would remain valid and is felt, in different ways, by nearly all scholars. (13) Latest publication of the relevant letters in *Dürer. Schriftlicher Nachlass* (ed. H.

Rupprich), I, 1956, pp. 61 ff.; textual quotation is from this edition. (14) M. Thausing, *Albert Dürer. His life and works* (transl. F. A. Eaton) 1882, II, pp. 8–9. Thausing confused the provenance of the Prague copy with that of No. 5592. (15) See his article in *The Dürer Society* (5th series) 1902, pp. 4–5. (16) *Loc. cit.* (17) *Loc. cit.* (18) On this point, see especially Panofsky, *loc. cit.* Altogether, the argument that such differentiation was made at the period is not very satisfactory. (19) *Loc. cit.* He instances for example Dürer's exaggeration of the number of heads in the *Assumption of the Virgin* he was painting for Heller: Dürer speaks of there being 'almost a hundred' of these, whereas there are in fact about thirty. (20) Rupprich ed., *op. cit.*, p. 66: 'So ichs ainen machen solt, nemb ich nit vnder 50 fl . . .'. (21) Rupprich ed., *op. cit.*, p. 68. (22) Rupprich ed., *op. cit.*, p. 72: 'Herr Jörg Tausy (*i.e.* Thurzo) hat sich von jhme selbst erbotten, in der mass, fleiss vnd gröss dieser taffel (*i.e.* the *Assumption* for Heller) ein Maria bildt zu machen, in ainer landschafft. Dauon wolle er mir geben 400 fl.' He goes on to say he refused the commission. The *Assumption* was only very slightly larger than No. 5592, as Panofsky points out in discussing this passage; for him the discrepancy in price between Thurzo's proposed commission and the *Maria bildt* indicates studio handling on the latter, not a different scale of picture. (23) See the Bishop's letter of 30 July 1511, Rupprich ed., *op. cit.*, p. 256. (24) It is to be noticed that his opinion of 1902 (*op. cit.*, note 15) was rather less favourable to the picture than at the time of his writing in 1945 (see general reference). See also in support of Dürer's authorship, but not execution, T. Sturge Moore, *Albert Dürer*, 1905, p. 212. (25) E. Flechsig, *Albrecht Dürer*, 1928, I, pp. 395 ff. (26) H. Tietze and E. Tietze-Conrat, *Kritisches Verzeichnis der Werke Albrecht Dürers*, II, 1937, pp. 145 ff. (27) E. Panofsky, *Albrecht Dürer*, 1945 ed., II, pp. 10–11. (28) In the *Daily Telegraph*, 26 February 1902 and 14 June 1906. Phillips accepted the design as Dürer's, but not the execution. (29) See his comment in *The Burlington Magazine*, IX, 1906, p. 267. (30) It is perhaps worth recalling that the flesh areas, which do seem to have affinities with Baldung's handling, are considerably damaged and partly repainted. The present writer learns from Jan Lauts that Dr. Carl Koch is not prepared to see the hand of Baldung on any part of No. 5592. (31) See his review of the Burlington Fine Arts Club exhibition in *Repertorium für Kunstwissenschaft*, 1906, pp. 586–7. (32) G. Glück in Vienna *Jahrbuch*, 1909–10, pp. 16–17. (33) See his comments, which tend to be too drastic, in Klassiker der Kunst *Dürer*, n.d. (4th ed.), p. 421; he reproduces No. 5592, p. 98. Cf. also F. Winkler, *Albrecht Dürer*, 1957, p. 208, note 1. (34) Reproduced in V. Scherer, Klassiker der Kunst *Dürer*, 1904, p. 40. The picture was included in the Dürer exhibition, Nuremberg, 1928, no. 75 as an original by Dürer. The Madonna apparently appears in whitish mantle, but this seems to be re-painting; a good deal of further repaint is recorded on the picture. (35) Referred to by M. W. Brockwell, *op. cit.*, p. 109; see *The Dürer Society (Index . . . , vols. I–X, 1898–1908)*, 1911, p. 64, noting that this picture was exhibited at Linz in 1908. Cf. also F. Winkler in Klassiker der Kunst *Dürer*, n.d. (4th ed.), p. 421. A reproduction is said to have been published by H. Ubell in *Erdgeist*, 1904, p. 150. The picture seems always to have been recognized as a copy. (36) So Brockwell, *op. cit.*, p. 108, with a reference apparently to J. Heller, *Das Leben und die Werke Albrecht Dürer's*, 1827, p. 260. Heller records merely the immediate provenance which follows in the text above and says nothing of the 'exchange from a relative at Nuremberg' for which Brockwell presumably had another source. The provenance given in the B.F.A.C. exhibition catalogue, 1906, accords with Brockwell. (37) Heller, *loc. cit.* (38) Information from a letter of Desvignes (of 1872) in the Gallery archives. Brockwell, *loc. cit.*, gives further details of the acquisition which are not supported by Desvignes' letter. (39) See the note 38 above. (40) Brockwell, *loc. cit.*

Adam ELSHEIMER

1578–1610

Baptized at Frankfort, 18 March 1578.[1] He was probably trained under, and certainly influenced by, Philipp Uffenbach at Frankfort.[2] At a date not established but *ca.* 1598 he seems to have left there for Munich,[3] and perhaps later that year was in Venice; he is said to have worked at Venice under Rottenhammer.[4] By 1600 he was at Rome[5] where he remained for the rest of his life. He married in 1606.[6] Died at Rome, 11 December 1610.[7]

The few dates conjectured with any probability in Elsheimer's life are not very firmly established; the dates of his departure from Frankfort, arrival in Munich, arrival in Venice, departure from Venice and arrival in Rome are all conjectural to some extent in the present state of knowledge. So are such stylistic questions as the exchange of influences between Elsheimer and Bril.

REFERENCES: *General:* H. Weizsäcker, *Adam Elsheimer, Der Maler von Frankfurt,* I, 1936; II, 1952.
In text: (1) The document published by Weizsäcker in Prussian *Jahrbuch,* 1910, p. 203. The discovery of it, thus correcting the previous supposition of 1574, published by F. Gwinner, *Kunst und Künstler in Frankfurt am Main* (*Zusätze und Berichtigungen*) 1867, p. 14. (2) That he was a follower of Uffenbach is stated first by Sandrart, cf. *Academie* (ed. A. Peltzer), 1925, p. 160. (3) A drawing (Brunswick) signed 'Adamus Ehlsheimer von frankfurrt' may perhaps provide some evidence for Elsheimer being in Munich; see the discussion in Weizsäcker, *op. cit.,* I, pp. 31 ff. (4) This is stated in the inscription under his portrait (by Hollar) in Jan Meyssens' *Images de divers hommes d'esprit sublime,* 1649, reproduced in Weizsäcker, *op. cit.* (Plates), pl. 1. Rottenhammer's name is replaced by that of Uffenbach in the 1661 publication of Hollar's portrait in Cornelis de Bie's *Gulden Cabinet.* See Weizsäcker, *op. cit.,* I, p. 315, note 7. (5) A drawing (Dresden) signed 'Adam Ehlsheim(er) in Rom 1600' (reproduced in Weizsäcker, *op. cit.,* Plates, pl. 4 [no. 5]). (6) Published by F. Noack in *Kunstchronik,* 1909–10 (no. 32), cols. 513 ff. (7) Noack, *loc cit.*

1014 S. LAWRENCE PREPARED FOR MARTYRDOM

At the right background a horseman carrying a banner inscribed: *S.P.Q.* The pedestal of the statue of Hercules extreme right is inscribed: *FA | OE(?) | HE*
Copper, $10\frac{1}{2} \times 8\frac{1}{8}$ (0·267 × 0·206).
In good condition; there are a few very minor paint losses.

S. Lawrence was martyred at Rome under the Prefect Decius in 258. The figure seated at the upper left of No. 1014 seems more likely meant as an Emperor.[1] Elsheimer appears to have added to the story of S. Lawrence the implication that the saint was martyred for refusing to worship false gods; according to the generally accepted account S. Lawrence was martyred for refusing to reveal the supposed treasures of the Church (cf. also No. 3665 of this catalogue, Circle of the Master of S. Ursula).

The statue of Hercules in No. 1014 was identified by Weizsäcker as an unmistakable derivation from the Farnese Hercules; the derivation is no doubt conscious but not very close. Interpretation of the letters on the pedestal is not easy; perhaps they are vaguely intended to be Greek and the second line might then begin with a capital theta (*i.e.* ΘΕΟΣ). The last word is no doubt for Hercules or Heracles. The building behind the statue was identified by Weizsäcker as based on the ruins of the temple of Vespasian in the Forum. In the pose of the angel appearing with a palm he supposed a derivation from Raphael's angels in the S. Maria della Pace fresco. This angel is in fact a very close derivative from the angel in a Raphael School fresco, *The Martyrdom of S. Cecilia*, a composition easily available through Marcantonio Raimondi's engraving of it.[2]

The design of No. 1014 was engraved by Soutman and it is reasonable to suppose that No. 1014 was the basis for this. Though popular, the composition seems recorded in an original Elsheimer only by No. 1014. Drost proposed a date *ca.* 1602–3 for it,[3] but Weizsäcker seemed to place it earlier, even before the Rome period which the use of Roman motifs as adduced by him makes doubtful. The present writer doubts if No. 1014 can possibly be much before 1600, and a period around that date seems likely.

The picture is one of those queried by Longhi who has suggested it might be by a Netherlandish artist, possibly Lastman.[4] This is not an acceptable attribution for No. 1014, and Longhi's suggestion has already been rejected by Benedict Nicolson.[5]

DRAWING : A drawing at Budapest by Elsheimer (unrelated probably to No. 1014) shows the Oriental at the right.[6]

COPIES : There are many and the list does not attempt completeness.[7] Old copies are at Vienna and Innsbruck. Less close derivatives are at Aschaffenburg and Speier. Copies were in anonymous London sales, 28 November 1951 (lot 63) and 14 October 1955 (lot 101). A close copy, signed A (or L) Schomaker is in the Gemeentelijk Museum, Roermond.[8] A copy, omitting the emperor and attendant at the left, in an anonymous sale, London, 10 October 1958 (lot 112).

ENGRAVINGS : In the same direction by P. Soutman[9] (mentioned above); by B. H. Lengin. An anonymous engraving in the reverse direction is recorded.

PROVENANCE : Conceivably in the Goodall sale, London, 9 April (second day), 1772 (lot 37).[10] Wynn Ellis bequest, 1876.

REPRODUCTION : *Illustrations, Continental Schools*, 1937, p. 108.

REFERENCES : *General:* Weizsäcker, *op. cit.*, I, pp. 70 ff.; II, no. 37.
In text: (1) It is a point often mentioned in versions of the S. Lawrence story that the Emperor (*i.e.* Valerian) was absent from Rome at the time; he in fact was in prison abroad. (2) The fresco, in the chapel of Villa Magliana near Rome, is referred to by Mrs. Jameson, *Sacred and Legendary Art*, 1883 ed., II, pp. 644–5. Marcantonio's engraving is Bartsch, no. 117. (3) W. Drost, *Adam Elsheimer und sein Kreis*, 1933, p. 58, note 31. (5) *Hendrick Terbrugghen*, 1958, p. 59. (6) A reproduction in W. Bode, *Adam Elsheimer, der romischer Maler deutscher Nation*, 1920, p. 4 (wrongly as at Berlin). (7) Weizsäcker, II, no. 37, for further copies and some details

concerning those not otherwise commented upon here. Additionally may
be mentioned: a version recorded in 1779 in the collection of August
Gottfried Schwalb at Hamburg (letter of 1949 from Dr. N. von Holst in the
Gallery archives); another in an inventory of 1781 of pictures belonging to the
Comte de Provence. Conceivably still another version belonged to Martin
Tupper (letter of 1876 in the Gallery archives). A version of the subject recorded
in Sir Henry Bruce collection, Down-hill, Londonderry, in 1821: Neale's *Seats*,
IV (1st series), 1821. (8) Letter of 1952 from M. K. J. Smeets in the Gallery
archives; this painter is perhaps to be identified with Andries Schomaker or
Schoemaker (1660–1735). (9) A reproduction in Weizsäcker, I (Plates) Pl. 26.
(10) Referred to by Weizsäcker, *op. cit.*, II, p. 195. Weizsäcker under his no. 37
linked No. 1014 with a picture of the subject referred to by Sandrart as in Count
Johann von Nassau-Zweibrücken's collection [cf., for example, A. R. Peltzer,
Joachim von Sandrarts Academie, . . . , 1925, p. 161], but in view of the many old
copies of No. 1014 this was perhaps to interpret too literally Sandrart's 'welches
original . . .'.

1424   TOBIAS AND THE ARCHANGEL RAPHAEL
       RETURNING WITH THE FISH

Copper, $7\frac{5}{8} \times 10\frac{7}{8}$ (0·193 × 0·276).

In general in quite good condition. Under the paint surface but
visible to the naked eye are some engraved(?) geometrical patterns
which cover most of the picture area but which have no relation to the
composition.

The subject, from the Book of *Tobit* in the Apocrypha, was treated
by Elsheimer in a number of compositions. Two of these were engraved
in reverse by Count Goudt and are known respectively as the 'small'
and the 'large' Tobias, the latter composition being approximately the
same as that of No. 1424.

In general No. 1424 has not been accepted as the original from which
Goudt engraved, nor always as by Elsheimer. Sir Walter Armstrong is
recorded as having suggested Claes Moeyaert as its painter[1]; Drost
ascribed it to Johann Heinrich Roos whose hand he was able to recognize on the picture[2]; Weizsäcker's opinion about No. 1424 seems
to have remained slightly dubious though he had earlier inclined to
accept it as at least studio work and included it is his catalogue of
originals by Elsheimer. Bode seems to have supposed it an original but
damaged,[3] an opinion also considered as a possibility some time ago by
Martin Davies.[4]

It is difficult to believe that No. 1424 can have been the basis for
Goudt's engraving of 1613, so marked are the differences between the
two.[5] Nevertheless, if the compositions claimed in other cases as
originals for Goudt's engravings are accepted, some divergences are
certainly to be expected[6]; in the case of No. 1424, however, they seem
too marked. A version closer to the engraving is a picture at Copenhagen,[7] but the quality of this seems to suggest that it was rather a
derivative than an original. Whatever its status, the status of No. 1424
need not be affected.

The quality of No. 1424 appears to the present writer definitely high enough to make it plausibly an original by Elsheimer, perhaps a slightly varied repetition of the version recorded by Goudt's engraving. The technique seems a little unusual, conceivably through damage of some sort. Presumably No. 1424 would be late work.

It is to be noted that this design, unlike the 'small' Tobias, did not prove so popular for pastiches and copies.[8]

DRAWINGS: A drawing, recorded when in the Charles Clarke collection, which reproduces the chief part of the composition is doubtfully by Elsheimer.[9] The landscape background of No. 1424 is the subject of a drawing recorded in the Robert von Hirsch collection, Bâle.[10]

ENGRAVING: A related engraving by Goudt is mentioned above.[11]

VERSIONS: A 'large' Tobias painting is mentioned in a Leyden legal document of 1673.[12] That at Copenhagen is mentioned above; another is recorded in the Ivan Traugott collection, Stockholm.

PROVENANCE: Possibly in the Dr. Richard Mead sale, London, 21 March 1754 (lot 49) bought by Whood for Beckford (i.e. William Beckford, senior). In the William Beckford (junior) sale, London, 27 February 1802 (lot 26) bought by Seguier. George Watson Taylor collection by 1819 when lent to the British Institution (no. 20); Watson Taylor sale, London, 14 June 1823 (lot 31)[13] bought by Thwaites. In the E. Phipps collection by 1854 when seen by Waagen[14]; Phipps sale, London, 25 June 1859 (lot 40), bought by Henry Farrer. By 1879 in the collection of Samuel Sandars, when lent to the Royal Academy (no. 239); Sandars bequest, 1894.

REPRODUCTION: *Illustrations, Continental Schools*, 1937, p. 108.

REFERENCES: *General:* Weizsäcker, *op. cit.*, I, pp. 122 ff; II, no. 9.
   In text: (1) Undated letter (but pre-1916) in the Gallery archives. (2) W. Drost, *Adam Elsheimer und sein Kreis*, 1933, p. 87, as of higher quality than the Copenhagen version (see below in text) but farther from Elsheimer's spirit. (3) Compare his article in the Prussian *Jahrbuch*, 1880, p. 254. (4) When reviewing Drost, *op. cit.*, in *The Burlington Magazine*, LXIV, 1934, p. 290. (5) A reproduction in Weizsäcker, *op. cit.*, 1936, I (Plates), pl. 54. (6) Thus there are divergences between the Madrid *Mocking of Ceres* (Weizsäcker, *op. cit.*, pl. 90) and Goudt's engraving (Weizsäcker, pl. 91), the most striking of which is the alteration in the child's head; conceivably here Goudt was following Elsheimer's etching not painting. (7) Weizsäcker, pl. 56, and II, p. 14, as a copy. (8) For instance, the copy of the subject after Elsheimer by Princess Louise which belonged to Charles I was presumably not this design, as supposed by Henry and Margaret Ogden, *English Taste in Landscape in the Seventeenth Century*, 1955, pp. 31 and 35, note 7; since that was entitled 'Tobias and the Angel crossing a ford' it would almost certainly be after the 'small' Tobias design. (9) Published by A. M. Hind in *The Burlington Magazine*, XLVIII, 1926, p. 192, as by Elsheimer, but not convincingly. (10) Weizsäcker, pl. 57. (11) There is a derived etching from this by Seghers; for reproduction cf. G. Knuttel, *Hercules Seghers Palet Serie*, post-1940), p. 27. An engraving by L. Vosterman of the foreground figures only (1659), after Goudt, also exists. (12) Further, cf. Weizsäcker, *op. cit.*, II, p. 14. (13) Weizsäcker, *op. cit.*, II, p. 14 raised the point that this provenance is confused since Passavant, *Kunstreise* . . . , 1833, p. 152, refers to the picture as still at Fonthill, while Waagen, *Treasures of Art* . . . 1854, II, p. 229, mentions the E. Phipps picture (*i.e.* No. 1424, see further under Provenance) as ex-Beckford and ex-Watson Taylor. In fact Beckford must have had two versions of the subject by Elsheimer, the 'large' and the 'small' Tobias, the second of which was seen by Passavant and which in fact is mentioned as in the Belvedere

at Fonthill in an MS. inventory of 1844 following Beckford's death. This
picture passed into the Hamilton collection (Beckford's daughter had married
the Duke of Hamilton) and was presumably in the Hamilton Palace sale,
London, 17 June 1882 (lot 64), in which case it is the picture now belonging to
Lady Martin; cf. further the catalogue (either ed.) of the exhibition at Wilden-
stein, London, 1955, *Artists in 17th Century Rome*, pp. 48 ff. (14) *Treasures of
Art in Great Britain*, 1854, II, p. 229.

3535   S. PAUL ON MALTA

At the left the saint holding the viper in his right hand.
Copper, $6\frac{5}{8} \times 8\frac{3}{8}$ ($0 \cdot 17 \times 0 \cdot 213$).
In good condition.

The subject, which is not very common, derives from the Acts of the
Apostles xxviii, 2–3.[1] The shipwreck of S. Paul took place by day, but
Elsheimer has chosen to show the scene by night. The viper came out
of the fire and fastened on the saint's hand: that he was unharmed by it
convinced the people he was a god.

No. 3535 is probably work from early in Elsheimer's Rome years,
presumably *ca.* 1600 (but after No. 1014 of this catalogue?). The treatment shows affinities with a picture at Munich, the *Burning of Troy*.[2]
For the night effects in such pictures Drost prefers to see a prototype
in Holbein's *Nativity* at Freiburg rather than in Caravaggio's work.[3]

A version of the same subject as No. 3535, but a different composition,
is at Leningrad.[4] This has sometimes been attributed to Elsheimer: an
attribution accepted by Drost[5] but rejected by Weizsäcker.[6]

PROVENANCE: 'The shipwreck of St. Pablo (Paul?) small, by the hand of
Adam' is mentioned in a note, given to and endorsed by Dudley Carleton, by
James Baptista Cresentio [*sic*] possibly of *ca.* 1614.[7] No doubt among the
pictures bequeathed by Sir Paul Methuen († 1757) to his cousin Paul Methuen
of Corsham House, Wilts.[8] In the Paul Methuen collection, Grosvenor Street,
London, in 1761.[9] Later at Corsham House.[10] Lent by Lord Methuen to the
British Institution, 1857 (no. 67); to the Burlington Fine Arts Club, 1906
(no. 65). Lord Methuen sale, London, 13 May 1920 (lot 16), bought by Burns.
Presented by Walter Burns, 1920.

REPRODUCTION: *Illustrations, Continental Schools*, 1937, p. 109.

REFERENCES: *General:* Weizsäcker, I, pp. 177 ff.; II, no. 31.
   In text: (1) Some treatments of the subject nearly contemporary with
Elsheimer, and later, are listed by A. Pigler, *Barockthemen*, 1956, I, pp. 392 ff.
(2) Weizsäcker, I (Plates), pl. 87. (3) Drost, *op. cit.*, pp. 42–3. (4) Weizsäcker,
II, pl. 37. (5) *Op. cit.*, pp. 49–50. Drost incidentally is wrong in saying this
picture is on copper; it is on wood. (6) *Op. cit.*, II, pp. 104–5. (7) See further
W. Noël Sainsbury, *Original Unpublished Papers illustrative of the life of . . .
Rubens*, 1859, p. 355. (8) On the reverse of No. 3535 is engraved (upside down):
Costó mil doblones en Amberes (*i.e.* Antwerp). It is perhaps a point in connection
with this that Sir Paul Methuen apparently bought most of his pictures abroad
and, in view of the indication of a Spanish provenance, that he served as
ambassador in Spain. (9) Dodsley's, *London and its Environs*, 1761, III, p. 98.
(10) For instance, cf. S. H. Spiker, *Travels . . .* 1820, II, p. 131 and J. D.
Passavant, *Kunstreise . . .* , 1833, p. 221. There is a later reference to it in
Waagen, *Galleries and Cabinets of Art . . .* 1857, p. 394.

3904 THE BAPTISM OF CHRIST

Right foreground S. Peter removing the coin from the fish; extreme left background Christ summoning S. Peter from his boat. At the top of the picture God the Father sending down the Dove.

Copper, $11\frac{1}{16} \times 8\frac{1}{4}$ (0·281 × 0·21).

In very good condition.

The conflation of the three incidents into one scene is very unusual and the iconography seems to be peculiar to Elsheimer. There can be no doubt that the right-hand foreground figure is S. Peter removing from the fish the coin that became the tribute money (as based on S. Matthew xvii, 27) and Weizsäcker was wrong in thinking the figure merely a man removing his shoe.

The treatment of the whole composition shows marked Venetian influences, specifically those of Tintoretto and Veronese, as Elsheimer authorities have agreed in emphasizing. No doubt these influences were sieved through Rottenhammer to Elsheimer, and No. 3904 is strong evidence for presuming that Elsheimer did study under Rottenhammer at Venice. It would therefore be likely that No. 3904 was ca. 1598 and probably pre-1600; these reasonable limits are accepted by most, if not all, authorities.[1]

A very similar style picture by Elsheimer is the *Rest on the Flight* at Berlin.[2]

PROVENANCE: Probably in Anonymous sale, London, 27 March (second day), 1779 (lot 70), bought by Shriber; probably in the Sir Joshua Reynolds sale, London, 14 March (fourth day), 1795 (lot 27), bought by Dermer.[3] Probably in the Booth etc. sale, London, 25 April 1812 (lot 132), bought by Bowden. In the George Smith sale, London, 27 May 1882 (lot 16), bought by Wagner. Henry Wagner collection, lent to the Burlington Fine Arts Club, 1906 (no. 67). Presented by Henry Wagner, 1924.

REPRODUCTION: *Illustrations, Continental Schools*, 1937, p. 109.

REFERENCES: *General:* Weizsäcker, *op. cit.*, I, pp. 66–7; II, no. 18.

In text: (1) *i.e.* Bode, *op. cit.*, 1920, p. 44; Drost, *op. cit.*, pp. 38 ff. No. 3904 is another picture which Longhi has inclined to attribute to—possibly—Lastman, cf. *Proporzioni*, I, 1943, p. 45, note 31. The attribution is particularly unconvincing. (2) It is Weizsäcker, I (Plates), pl. 22. (3) These identifications can be fairly confidently accepted in view of the absence of copies and versions of the subject. The identification of No. 3904 with Reynolds' picture was proposed in the editorial of *The Burlington Magazine*, LXXXVII, 1945, p. 267.

GERMAN School, XVI century

2158 PORTRAIT OF A WOMAN

Bust length, facing left.

Oak, approximately $16\frac{1}{8} \times 11$ (0·41 × 0279); uneven edges and a piece cut away at the bottom right-hand corner.

A wreck, very extensively damaged and partly repainted.

No. 2158 seems to be the remains of a sixteenth-century German picture; in the 1929 catalogue as German School, withdrawn from exhibition. In the Krüger catalogue as supposedly by Holbein the Younger. The style is perhaps vaguely near that of Hans Muelich (Mielich) but no further comment is possible.

PROVENANCE: In the Krüger Collection, Minden, by 1848.[1] Bought with the majority of the Krüger collection, 1854. Later on long loan to the National Gallery of Ireland, Dublin.[2]

REPRODUCTION: A negative exists at the Gallery.

REFERENCES: (1) Krüger catalogue 1848, Part II, No. 5. (2) 1857–1926; not apparently catalogued before the 1915 catalogue (where listed as at Dublin).

GERMAN(?) SCHOOL, XVII century

2156   S. CHRISTOPHER CARRYING THE INFANT CHRIST

In the sky some demons. At the left a hermit; at the right a group of people seated on the river bank.
Copper, $3\frac{7}{8} \times 5\frac{3}{8}$ (0·098 × 0·136).
In quite good condition.

S. Christopher, a giant, was martyred in the fourth century. A hermit told him to carry wayfarers across a dangerous river, presumably the hermit who appears at the left here. The group at the right are perhaps waiting to be carried across.[1]

No. 2156 seems to be a seventeenth-century picture and there is some faint influence of Elsheimer. It might conceivably be Flemish and in the Krüger collection was said to be by 'Franck'.[2] Since entry into the Gallery it has been called German and the attribution is doubtfully accepted here. It is in the 1929 Catalogue as withdrawn from exhibition. The picture is anyway of poor quality and virtually unattributable.

PROVENANCE: In the Krüger Collection, Minden, by 1848.[3] Bought with the majority of the Krüger Collection, 1854. Later on long loan to the National Gallery of Ireland, Dublin.[4]

REPRODUCTION: A negative exists at the Gallery.

REFERENCES: (1) The story of S. Christopher is told in La Légende Dorée (Garnier ed.) I, pp. 194 ff. According to that version there was nobody else about when S. Christopher carried the Infant across the river. (2) Presumably for Francken; the picture is not by any known member of that family. (3) Krüger catalogue, 1848, Part II, no. 16. (4) 1857–1926; it first appears apparently in the 1915 catalogue (as German School, lent to Dublin).

Ascribed to the GERMAN SCHOOL

2157   VIRGIN AND CHILD WITH AN ANGEL IN A LANDSCAPE

Oak, $9\frac{1}{2} \times 6\frac{3}{4}$ (0·240 × 0·172), arched top.
In quite good condition under discoloured varnish.

The picture was attributed to the Netherlandish School in the Krüger catalogue but has been called German since acquisition by the Gallery. It is in the 1929 catalogue as withdrawn from exhibition. The picture seems to be intended to pass as a fifteenth-century work, either of the Netherlandish or German School, and is catalogued here for convenience. It does not seem an old picture and there can be little doubt that it is a fake; it is of very poor quality.

PROVENANCE: In the Krüger collection, Minden, by 1848.[1] Purchased with the majority of the Krüger collection, 1854. Later on long loan to the National Gallery of Ireland, Dublin.[2]

REPRODUCTION: A negative exists at the Gallery.

REFERENCES: (1) Krüger Catalogue, 1848, Part II, no. 18. (2) From 1857–1926; it is first listed apparently in the 1915 catalogue (as German School, on loan to Dublin).

Wolfgang HEIMBACH
Active 1636–1678

Probably in full *Wolfgang Johann Heimbach*.[1] The date of birth is not known but the place was almost certainly the village of Ovelgönne, near Oldenburg, where his father is first mentioned in 1611–12. The painter was a deaf mute.

The first dated picture, the *Wedding Feast* (Kunsthalle, Bremen) apparently bears the inscription: *Ovelgönne Anno 1636, Bremen 1637*.[2] Dutch influence on that picture is obvious and Heimbach is recorded by a contemporary historian as having studied when young under a painter in Holland.[3] The same source records him as having later spent twelve years in Italy; a portrait of *Pope Innocent X* (Statens Museum, Copenhagen) is dated 1645 and a letter of 1646 from Grand Prince Ferdinand of Tuscany speaks of him as then in Italy. Heimbach probably reached Italy *ca.* 1640 and in August 1651 was in Prague. He was back at Ovelgönne by February 1652 and was later that year taken into the service of Count Anton Günther of Oldenburg for a probationary period of six months, after which his employment lapsed.

Apparently in 1653 Heimbach was in Copenhagen, where he became one of the Court painters to Frederick III; in an undated letter to the king, asking for leave to return home, he says he has been in the royal service eight and a half years. That he was still in Copenhagen for at least part of 1662 is proved by the inscription on No. 1243 below. He is recorded at Oldenburg in 1665 and 1666. On the evidence of inscribed pictures he was again in Copenhagen in 1667, at Ovelgönne in 1669 and still living in 1678 (signed and dated *Portrait of a Man*, Schloss Blankenburg).

Heimbach painted portraits, genre scenes and a few religious pictures, as well as copying pictures by some of his Dutch contemporaries.[4]

REFERENCES: *General: G. Göttsche, Wolfgang Heimbach*, 1935, where the relevant documents are quoted.

In text: (1) The fact of a further initial, almost certainly J, in many of Heimbach's monograms (as on No. 1243) seems not to have been remarked. He signs a document (when signing with his father, Wolf Heimbach): *Wolf. Gio. Heimbach, Pittore* (cf. Göttsche, *op. cit.*, p. 18, and her comment, p. 17, notes 1 and 2); conceivably, but by no means necessarily, he adopted the name in Italy. (2) Göttsche, *op. cit.*, cat. no. 2. The Bremen catalogue of 1925 is presumably wrong in reading the first date '1635'; the handbook of 1954 (p. 26) merely records the picture as of 1636. (3) See Göttsche *op. cit.*, pp. 13 ff., quoting from J. J. Winckelmann's *Oldenburgische Chronik* who says that at the time of writing (date not known) Heimbach is 'ein Mann von 50 Jahren'. (4) For additions to the *œuvre* since Göttsche, *op. cit.*, cf. H. Gerson in *Kunsthistorische Mededelingen*, 1946, pp. 8 ff.; S. J. Gudlaugsson, *loc. cit.*, 1948, pp. 4–5 and pp. 11–12, and A. Pigler, *ibid.*, pp. 8 ff.

1243 PORTRAIT OF A YOUNG MAN

Waist length, to the right. Behind, the view of a harbour with shipping.

Signed on the balustrade bottom right: *Cop: CHJ(?)Fe.* (in ligature) *W 166* | 2.

Oak, $19\frac{1}{2} \times 14\frac{1}{8}$ (0·495 × 0·359) oval. Painted up to the edges all round. In very good condition under discoloured varnish. *Pentimenti* in the hat.

Similar monograms occur elsewhere in Heimbach's work, sometimes with minor variations. The C of his monograms was at one time said to stand for Christian, erroneously supposed one of Heimbach's names; it is probably for *Contrafactor*.[1] The doubtful letter of the monogram is probably J; it has been explained in the biography above that this is probably for Johann. The abbreviation *Cop.* for Copenhagen occurs elsewhere on Heimbach's pictures; the view in No. 1243 is probably intended as Copenhagen, but the detail is not sufficient to establish this. The flags on the boats do not seem of any significance.

No. 1243 was acquired and first catalogued as Dutch School. Only later was the monogram understood; the picture appears as by Heimbach in the 1929 catalogue. Göttsche, who suggested the sitter might be a Danish merchant, emphasized the picture's documentary interest as the latest record of Heimbach's activity in Denmark on his first stay.[2]

PROVENANCE: Bought from Meredith Roberts, London, 1888.[3]

REPRODUCTION: *Illustrations, Continental Schools*, 1937, p. 153.

REFERENCES: (1) See Thieme-Becker *Lexikon*, XVI, *ad vocem*. (2) *Op. cit.*, pp. 18 and 63. It is Göttsche's catalogue, p. 76 (no. 45). (3) Apparently as Dutch School and of 'Van Tromp': letters in the Gallery archives.

Hans HOLBEIN the Younger
1497/8–1543

Born at Augsburg, 1497–8,[1] son of Hans Holbein the Elder under whom he was trained. At Bâle by 1515,[2] where his elder brother

Ambrosius is also recorded as a painter; at Lucerne from 1517–19,[3] with probably a visit to Northern Italy during this period.[4] He became a member of the painters' guild at Bâle on 25 September 1519,[5] and a citizen there on 3 July 1520.[6] A visit to France in 1524 is recorded.[7] A letter of 29 August 1526 from Erasmus to Ægidius at Antwerp speaks of a painter (clearly Holbein) setting out for England.[8] Sir Thomas More in a letter of 18 December 1526, to Erasmus records Holbein as in London.[9]

The painter returned to Bâle in 1528 [10] but by 1532 was again in London,[11] where he settled. The date of his entering Henry VIII's service is not known, but he is referred to as a royal servant in 1536.[12] In March 1538 he was in Brussels (see further under No. 2475 below) and later the same year in France whence he briefly visited Bâle.[13] He made his will in London, 7 October 1543, and a document of 29 November 1543 appended to it records him as recently dead.[14]

Holbein practised as painter, draughtsman, book-illustrator, and executed designs for jewellery, pageants, etc., as well as fresco decorations. In England his pictures were chiefly portraits.

REFERENCES: *General:* A. Woltmann, *Holbein und seine Zeit,* 1874–6 ed. A. B. Chamberlain, *Hans Holbein the Younger,* 1913. P. Ganz, *The Paintings of Hans Holbein the Younger,* 1950. The documents on Holbein's Bâle activity were published by E. His in *Jahrbücher für Kunstwissenschaft,* 1870, pp. 115 ff. Otherwise documents concerning him have not been fully collected.

In text: (1) A drawing (Berlin) by the elder Holbein of his two sons is dated 1511 and Hans is annotated as fourteen. Some Holbein self-portraits (cf. Ganz, *op. cit.,* nos 130–1) of 1542–3 give his age as forty-five. (2) Among other work, the painted table (Zürich) for Hans Baer of Bâle dated 1515, in which year Baer died: Ganz, *op. cit.,* no. 152. (3) Holbein was a member of the S. Luke's guild there, but the exact dates are lacking in the surviving copy of the lost original MS. list. He is first recorded at Lucerne in October, 1517, and last on 21 May 1519: see A. B. Chamberlain, *op. cit.,* I, pp. 64 and 78. (4) The evidence is purely stylistic, but very strong. (5) His, *op. cit.,* p. 116. (6) His, *op. cit.,* p. 118. (7) Letter of 3 June 1524 from Erasmus to Pirckheimer; see the quotation in P. Ganz, Klassiker der Kunst *Holbein,* 1912, p. 25. (8) Cited by Woltmann, *op. cit.,* I, p. 317. (9) The relevant passage quoted in U. Hegner, *Hans Holbein der Jüngere,* 1827, p. 189, note 2; further comment on the date of this letter in Chamberlain, *op. cit.,* I, p. 169. (10) On 29 August 1528 he bought a house in Bâle: His, *op. cit.,* p. 123, showing that Holbein really was in Bâle for the purchase. (11) The exact date not known, but certainly by 2 September 1532 when the Council at Bâle addressed a letter asking Holbein to return there. (12) Letter of that year from Nicolas Bourbon to Henry VIII's secretary, Solimar: cf. Woltmann, *op. cit.,* I, p. 404. (13) For the French journey, see A. B. Chamberlain in *The Burlington Magazine,* XXI, 1912, pp. 25 ff.; Holbein was in Bâle before 12 September 1538: cf. Woltmann, *op. cit.,* I, p. 456. (14) Documents and discussion by A. W. Franks in *Archaeologia,* xxxix, 1863, pp. 1 ff. and W. H. Black, *loc. cit.,* pp. 272 ff.

1314 JEAN DE DINTEVILLE AND GEORGES DE SELVE ('THE AMBASSADORS')

At the left Jean de Dinteville, wearing the order of Saint Michel. On his cap is a brooch ornamented with a skull[1]; the sheath of his dagger is inscribed: *ÆT. SVÆ* | 29. At the right Georges de Selve, his right arm resting on a book inscribed: *ÆTAT | IS SVÆ.* 25 (the *ae* of *suae* is a composite abbreviation). The large number of objects on the shelves of the what-not between the two men are described and discussed below. Across the mosaic floor in front a skull in perspective. The crucifix partly visible in the top left-hand corner of the picture inscribed: *IN. . .* Signed on the shadowed part of the floor at the lower left: *IOANNES | HOLBEIN | PINGEBAT | 1533.*

Oak, painted surface, $81\frac{1}{2} \times 82\frac{1}{2}$ ($2 \cdot 07 \times 2 \cdot 095$). Painted up to the edges except at the top.

In general in quite good condition. Splitting of the vertical panels which make up the support has caused some local damages, quite extensive in places. Dinteville's hands are not in very good state and the curtain behind the sitters has suffered damage and is in parts repainted. There are two *pentimenti* in Selve's cheek.

Jean de Dinteville (1504–55), Seigneur de Polisy, Bailly de Troyes, was five times French ambassador or diplomatic envoy to England, in particular from mid-February to mid-November, 1533. Another portrait of him occurs in a Dinteville family allegory by Félix Chrétien, *Moses and Aaron before Pharaoh*, of 1537.[2] He was painted as S. George by Primaticcio.[3] A probable drawing of him, by the hand known as Jean Clouet, also exists.[4] A portrait by Holbein at Berlin has sometimes been said to represent him, but clearly does not[5]; neither does a drawing at Windsor also once claimed as a portrait of him.[6]

Georges de Selve (1508/9–41) became Bishop of Lavaur in 1526 and was consecrated in 1534. He was several times ambassador to the Emperor, the Venetian Republic and the Holy See. He visited his friend Dinteville in London apparently before Easter, *i.e.* mid-April, 1533, *n.s.*, and had left before the end of May.

The identification of the sitters was made by Miss Hervey who also investigated and discovered most of the facts known about the picture, the objects in it and its provenance.

The mosaic pavement is a fairly exact copy of Abbot Ware's, still existing at Westminster Abbey.[7] On the picture the central circle contains a six-pointed star, and there are a few other minor differences from the original. However, it is quite clear that Holbein derived his floor from the Westminster Abbey pavement.

The principal objects on the lower shelf of the what-not are a lute with a broken string (the case is on the floor below), a case of lutes, an open hymn-book with music, a half-open book of arithmetic and a terrestrial globe. Miss Hervey's theory that these objects, and others in the picture, had each a symbolic meaning for the sitters, seems very likely. At the same time their significance could well be collective, intended to convey learning in general; one may cite the remarkably detailed still-life of Carpaccio's *S. Jerome in his Study* (Scuola degli Schiavoni, Venice), where a book has real music, etc. Such a very detailed still-life as that in No. 1314 is without a parallel in Holbein's other pictures, and the skull in the foreground (to be discussed below) can indeed hardly be explained as merely a whim of the painter's in such a commission.

The lute with a broken string is possibly intended as an emblem of division, though it is not clear whether it refers to the imminent parting of the two friends or whether—more probably—it has a political meaning. Political dissension is the meaning of Alciati's use of the emblem[8]; and there seems to be at least one other reference to dissension in the picture. There is also a possibility that the broken lute string is connected with the idea of a *vanitas* still-life.

The hymn-book with music has the following inscriptions (the lines not being kept separate): on the left-hand page:

XIX

KOm heiliger geyst herregott
erfüll mit deiner gnaden (gut)
deiner gleubgē hertz mut uñ sin
dein brüstig lib entzūd in ihn
O herr durch deines lichtes glast
zu dem glaubē versamlet hast
das volck aller welt zungē
(das sey) *dir herzu lob gesungen gesungen;*

on the right-hand page:

MEnsch wiltu leben seliglich
und bei Gott blibene (ewiglich)
Soltu halten die zehen gebot
die uns gebeut unser Gott unser (Gott),

and lower down, *D* followed by a damage. These hymns are Luther's renderings. On the left is the first verse of his version of the *Veni Creator Spiritus*. On the right the beginning of his 'Ten Commandments'. The *D* at the bottom stands for *Dein*; the next line over the page would be, *Dein Gott allein und Herr bin ich*. It is clear that the *Veni Creator Spiritus* is not meant to continue, but the single verse is an antiphon or introduction to the other. The book is a tenor part-book; as the melody of *Kom Heiliger Geist* is in the treble only the counterpoint is given but the melody of the other is in the tenor and is therefore given in the book. Since other objects in the picture are exactly copied from actual originals, Holbein no doubt copied an actual hymn-book—but the exact one seems not known. It is likely that it was some edition or derivative of Johann Walther's *Geystliche Gesangbüchlein*, first published in 1524; like the picture, Walther's text has *Glast* for the modern form of *Glantz*, and his number for *Mensch Wiltu . . .* is also XIX.

The original of the arithmetic book is known; it is Peter Apian's *Eyn newe unnd wohlgegründte underweysung aller Kauffmanss Rechnung*, 1527, shown in the picture half open at Book III, Q. 8, verso.[9]

Originals of the terrestrial globe also exist. They are ascribed to Johann

4—G.S.

Schöner and have sometimes been supposed to be those made by him at Nuremberg in 1523. A set of original gores was acquired and published by Henry Stevens as Schöner's[10]; they mark the voyage of Magellan which ended in 1522 but seem also to include facts known only later than 1523. The names on the Stevens or 'Munich' gores are not in capitals, but are otherwise repeated with extreme precision on the picture.

It is true that a part of the New World marked *Baccalaos* (*i.e.* Newfoundland) on the Stevens globe does not correspond with anything on Holbein's; but this area of the picture is anyway repainted. Apart from trivial corrections (such as v for u), the following are better readings than Miss Hervey's for what remains of some of Holbein's names (the names on the Stevens globe being given in brackets): ..SVLA ES... (Insula Espaliola), ANTIGLĮE INSVLA (Antiglie Insule), ISL.N... (Islan | dia), DESERTV MAG. V (Desertū magnū), NAY..... |RV.. (Naymano | rum reg:), BISERMINAR | VM TERRA (Bisermino |rum terra), TARTARIA TORQUEST(Ī?) (Tartaria Torquestē), CAMBE (IA?) (Cambeia), PERSARV̄ REG: (Persarū reg.), MESOPOTANIA (Mesopotamia), SIRIA (Syria), ...X.. | LEAMAN (Arabia Felix et Leaman), GINOIAE (Ginoia), HABESCH P. ESBITER.. ANNES (Habesch presbiter Ioannes), ETHIOPIA ṢVB EGIPTO (Ethiopia sub Egipto), SEILA (Seyla), NVBIE REGNV̄ (Nubie regnū), RIO DE GA... (Rio de Gaban), ANGRA DAS..DAS (Angra das Aldas), PONT' EVXIN' (Pōt' Euxin'), PERSIC' ET BESSRA SI: (Persic' et Bessara Si), ARABIC..SIN' (Arabic' Sin'), TROGLO | D... (Troglodite). To be added to Miss Hervey's list: GVZ... (Guzerath), ZAFA.. (Zafala), ...A (Quiola), MELINDA (Melinde), ...LA (Zazela), INDVS FL (Ind' fl). With two or three exceptions in odd corners, Holbein has put in all the names from the Stevens globe on his, so far as it is shown, even when the shadow or the perspective makes them almost illegible. The modern forms for them are given by Miss Hervey.[11]

An interesting point about Holbein's globe is that several names are added, which are not in the Stevens original. These are: POLISY, BARIS (*i.e.* Paris), LEON (*i.e.* Lyons), BAION (*i.e.* Bayonne), NORMĀ (*i.e.* Normandy), PRITANN | IA (*i.e.* Brittany), AVERN (*i.e.* Auvergne), BVRGVND, LANGVEDOC; ROMA, GENVA, SIN' ADRIATICVS; CASTIL, ARAGON, NAVAR, GRANA (*i.e.* Granada); SAXONIA, POLONIA, SERVIA. Holbein has also marked (but not named) the rivers Seine and Rhone, where on the Stevens globe there is nothing. The only one of these additions immediately comprehensible is Polisy, where Dinteville's château was situated. Some of the other names have more or less vague connections with the sitters; but in the execution at least Holbein had a fairly free hand (for no French Ambassador—or Bishop—would have thought of Baris and Prittany), and it is conceivable that some of the names were put in merely to avoid blank spaces on the map of Europe.

The objects[12] on the upper shelf of the what-not are: (1) a celestial globe, (2) a portable cylindrical sundial or Shepherd's dial, (3) a quadrant, behind (4) a kind of table quadrant, on which rests (5) an unidentified instrument, (6) a polyhedral sundial, and (7) Apian's Torquetum with Semissis. Nos. 2, 4, 5 and 6 reappear with slight variations in Holbein's portrait of Kratzer of 1528 in the Louvre.[13]

(1) The celestial globe is set for a latitude of 42° or 43° (which would mean the South of Europe). The constellations, as is normal at the time, are drawn in as animals, etc., the names of which are in most cases given. GALACIA (the Milky Way) is confused by Miss Hervey with the neighbouring constellation of the Hen, which she names the Cock (Gallina, now called Cygnus). The other inscriptions on the globe are: VVLTVR CADENS (*i.e.* Lyra), DRACO, CEPHEVS, PERSEVS, ANDROMEDA, (Cas)SIOPEIA, EQVVS PEGASVS, (Del-)PHINVS, VVLTVR VOLA(ns) (*i.e.* Aquila), PISCES, HERCVLES, AU(riga), VRS(a Min)O(r), (Ursa) MAIO(r).

(2) This instrument tells the time of day from the altitude of the sun, its design varying with the latitude at which it is required to be used. The style at the top is turned to the date of the month, and then placed facing the sun; the tip of the vertical shadow so cast gives the time, the curved lines representing the different hours. In the picture, the date seems to be set to about 11 April or 15 August; the elevation of the sun being the same at the two dates, the instrument makes no distinction, but as Selve came to London in April, 1533, the first is the more likely. It is doubtful, however, if a reading of the time is being taken, since the light (even supposing it is the sun) appears to be casting an oblique shadow. The engraved figures on the instrument, of which three are clearly visible, may be the signs of the Zodiac—the Ram, the Virgin and possibly the Bull.

(3) The quadrant is essentially an instrument for measuring angular altitudes; VMBRA VERSA corresponds with *Umbra Recta* (not shown), and refers to the 'scales of the shadows'.[14]

(6) The times marked on three of the faces of this polyhedral sundial are about 9.30, 10.30 and 10.30. The variations in the cast shadows are, of course, impossible; as the times indicated are not even the same, it is difficult to suppose anything except that different parts of the instrument were painted at different hours.[15] Inset in the top of the principal face is a magnetic compass, by means of which the instrument could be placed for use.

(7) The torquetum was an instrument for determining the position of celestial bodies; said to have been invented about 1260, it was perfected by Apian, a very similar instrument being engraved in his *Astronomicum Caesareum*, 1540. The inscriptions at right angles are AXIS SODIACI and LINEA (Ecliptic)A. The plumbline on the semissis or hanging semicircle measured the altitude; on the picture it is between 0° and 10°.

The problem remains whether all this extraordinary detail can possibly have been put into the picture without significance and what is the probable meaning of its presence. Wornum almost by accident drew attention to the heraldic effect of the picture, and he compared it with Holbein's 'Arms of Death' illustration where a death's head is in the

place of the distorted skull of No. 1314.[16] Later critics have taken up and
developed this suggestion.[17] It has sometimes been supposed that the
skull in the picture is a punning signature but this is exceedingly unlikely. The distortion of the skull can be paralleled to some extent by
other sixteenth-century optical distortions in pictures.[18] The object on
Dinteville's cap brooch is certainly a skull, as Miss Hervey proposed.
That Dinteville had adopted it as his device is therefore very possible,
and the occurrence of the two skulls can hardly be chance. Some
evidence for Dinteville's love of learned allusion may be found in the
fancy portrait of him as S. George by Primaticcio—for it is not immediately obvious why he should choose to be depicted as that saint—and
in the picture by Chrétien of the Dinteville brothers as Biblical per-
sonages in a scene of topical reference.

The symbolism of the skull in the picture as a *memento mori* of some
sort must, it seems, be accepted. Recently Baltrušaitis has developed
this idea for the complete still-life in the picture,[19] linking it particularly
with Cornelius Agrippa's *De incertitudine et vanitate scientiarum et
artium* . . . (1530), and Agrippa had already been mentioned in connection with the picture by Miss Hervey. The ideas Baltrušaitis puts forward are very interesting, even if they are not all of them totally
convincing.

Baltrušaitis compares the still life of No. 1314 with some marquetry
panels executed by Vincenzo dalle Vacche which show still life with, it
seems, very strong *vanitas* intentions: a skull, snuffed-out candles, etc.[20]
But the immense detail of the scientific objects, for example, in No. 1314
would seem to indicate interest in them for their own sake, as well as,
or instead of, metaphysical symbolism. Indeed, as has been pointed out
already, some of them appear also in Holbein's portrait of the astronomer
Kratzer (Louvre), where their relevance is immediately obvious.[21] And
that Holbein placed the name of Dinteville's château of Polisy on
the terrestrial globe might also perhaps be cited as some evidence
against the idea of a *vanitas* still-life and in favour rather of personal
associations.

No very satisfactory reason has yet been advanced why either Dinteville or the Bishop of Lavaur should have chosen Luther's rendering of
the *Veni Creator Spiritus*, nor why they should have Apian's German
arithmetic book.[22] But the present writer thinks these things must have
been inserted with a purpose, though the purpose may well no longer
be clear. Against the unlikelihood of the sitters' choosing any work by
Luther, it may be suggested that they may well not have been aware of
the author [sic] of what are after all only translations. The choice of the
Veni Creator Spiritus certainly seems to indicate an appeal for the Holy
Spirit to come, perhaps to heal dissension. Possibly Luther's text was
chosen simply because it represented the wider appeal of the vernacular
in place of the limited appeal of the Latin text: at the same time, the
sentiment of the original is unchanged and could be subscribed to by
Catholic and Protestant alike. The same is of course true of the Ten
Commandments.

DRAWINGS: Two drawings of the medal of S. Michael, probably preparatory to No. 1314, are at Bâle.[23]

COPY: A copy, with variations, of the upper half of the figure of Dinteville was in an anonymous sale, London, 6 February 1952 (lot 61).[24]

PROVENANCE: At Polisy, the château of Jean de Dinteville, whence removed to Paris in 1653 by Dinteville's great-great nephew, François de Cazillac, Marquis de Cessac.[25] In the Nicolas Beaujon, deceased, sale, Paris, 25 April *sqq.* 1787 (lot 16 *bis*); as it is not mentioned in Beaujon's inventory of January 1787, it was probably added to the sale, together with lot 16 (also a Dinteville picture) by his executor, Chrétien-François de Lamoignon, Marquis de Basville. This is all the more probable in that Basville had inherited at least one estate from his cousin Marie-Renée Voisin, granddaughter and heiress of the François de Cazillac who had owned the picture in the seventeenth century.[26] No. 1314 was bought at the Beaujon sale by the dealer J.-B. Lebrun who had sold it into England by 1792.[27] It was sold by Buchanan to the Earl of Radnor, 1808–9.[28] At Longford Castle. Exhibited at the Royal Academy, 1873 (no. 114).[29] Purchased from the 5th Earl of Radnor, together with Nos. 1315 and 1316, by special grant and with gifts from Charles Cotes, Sir E. Guiness, Bart. (Lord Iveagh) and Lord Rothschild, 1890.

REPRODUCTION: *Illustrations, Continental Schools*, 1937, p. 164.

REFERENCES: *General:* Mary F. S. Hervey, *Holbein's "Ambassadors"*, 1900. The attempt by W. F. Dickes, *Holbein's "Ambassadors" Unriddled*, 1903, to prove Miss Hervey wrong and to substitute different identifications for the sitters is misguided and unconvincing.

In text: (1) This had been claimed by Hervey, *op. cit.*, p. 201, and re-examination of the picture shows that the silver object on the gold brooch is indeed a miniature skull. (2) Published by Mary F. S. Hervey and R. Martin-Holland in *The Burlington Magazine*, XIX, 1911, pp. 48 ff.; further cf. C. Sterling's Catalogue of French Paintings in the Metropolitan Museum, 1955, pp. 44 ff. (3) See the exhibition catalogue *Triomphe du Maniérisme Européen*, Amsterdam, 1955, no. 101. (4) Published by Mary Hervey in *The Burlington Magazine*, V, 1904, p. 413. (5) It is catalogued in P. Ganz, *The Paintings of Hans Holbein*, 1950, no. 84 (Unknown Gentleman). (6) Cf. K. T. Parker, *Holbein Drawings at Windsor Castle*, 1945, cat. no. 32 (unknown). (7) See Hervey, *op. cit.*, pp. 225 ff.; and the Royal Commission on Historical Monuments: I, Westminster Abbey, 1924, p. 25. (8) As instanced by Hervey, *op. cit.*, p. 228 ff. (9) The original page reproduced by Hervey, *op. cit.*, p. 224. A possible significance for this book may be recorded, with reserves: the first word on the open page is *Diuidirt*, and it might therefore be, like the lute, a symbol of division. (10) They are reproduced by Hervey, *op. cit.*, facing p. 214. Apart from these gores, there exist two globes: one in the National Maritime Museum, Greenwich, the other in Anonymous sale (books), Sotheby, 20 April 1959 (lot 205), reproduction in the illustrated catalogue. (11) *Op. cit.*, pp. 215 ff. (12) Information about the astronomical instruments was kindly given by A. Barclay and W. E. Pretty of the Science Museum, during the 1939–45 war. (13) Ganz, *op. cit.*, no. 48. (14) A very similar quadrant is engraved in Apian's *Instrumentum Buch*, 1533, where it is called *Horarium Bilimbatum*. (15) It may be noted in this connection that the shadow of the skull in perspective, although no doubt correctly copied according to some distorting mirror or device, is quite different from all the other cast shadows in the picture. (16) R. N. Wornum, *Some Account of the life and works of Hans Holbein*, 1867, p. 181. Ironically enough, Wornum did not recognize the distorted skull on No. 1314 as a skull. (17) See for instance F. Grossmann in *The Burlington Magazine*, XCIII, 1951, p. 39, note 6. (18) For example, the perspective of Edward VI at the National Portrait Gallery (no. 1299): for this and others, see J. Byam Shaw in *Apollo*, 1927, ii, pp. 208 ff. and on the whole subject J. Baltrušaitis, *Anamorphoses*, 1955. (19) See the discussion in his *op.*

cit., p. 58 ff. (20) Reproduced by Baltrušaitis, *op. cit.*, p. 57. (21) Some of these
instruments might have been obtained by Holbein, or Dinteville, from Kratzer
who not only appears with four in his portrait but is also recorded to have made
several variants of the polyhedral sundial. Apian, whose name occurs often in
the text above, was also a maker of many of these instruments. (22) But see the
note 9 here. (23) Reproduced by Ganz, *Die Handzeichnungen Hans Holbeins des
Jüngeren*, vol. VI, no. 396 (pl. vi). (24) Attributed to J. Clouet, 'Portrait of a
Man, said to be the Comte d'Espinay . . .'. (25) The name given wrongly in
P. Ganz, *The Paintings of Hans Holbein*, 1950, cat. no. 74. (26) Hervey, *op. cit.*,
pp. 5 ff. (27) Engraved by J.-A. Pierron in Lebrun's *Galerie des Peintres
Flamands*, Part 12 (1790). (28) Hervey, *op. cit.*, p. 6. (29) As 'The Two Ambassa-
dors, believed to be Sir Thomas Wyatt and his Secretary.'

2475   CHRISTINA OF DENMARK, DUCHESS OF MILAN

Full length, in mourning robes. At the right a *cartellino* inscribed:
*Christine Daughter to Chri | stie(rne) k of Den(mark)... | of Lor(rai)ne.
and he (...) | Dutches of Milan.*

Oak, painted surface, 70½ × 32½ (1·79 × 0·825). Probably slightly cut
at both sides.

In fair condition; in the face, which is worn chiefly in the shadows,
it is partly repainted. The hands, though slightly rubbed and partly
retouched, are in better state and retain a considerable degree of their
original quality. The dress (originally purplish brown, not black) is a
good deal worn and repainted; there are retouchings on the coat but
both sleeves retain some original quality. The background and floor are
completely repainted. Originally the background was blue-green; it is
damaged and overlaid by Prussian blue. The new paint surrounds but
does not extend under the *cartellino*.

Christina, younger daughter of Christian II of Denmark and Isabella
of Austria, sister of Charles V, was born in 1522.[1] In 1533 she married by
proxy Francesco Maria Sforza, Duke of Milan, who died in 1535. She
retired to the court of her aunt, Mary of Hungary, at Brussels; and many
offers were made for her hand. Henry VIII of England was attempting
throughout 1538 and part of 1539, to negotiate a marriage with her,
which finally fell through. In 1541 she married François, Duc de Bar,
who succeeded his father as Duc de Lorraine in 1544 and died in 1545,
leaving Christina Regent of Lorraine. She was banished from the duchy
when the French occupied it in 1552, but later returned. After the death
of Henry VIII, she twice visited England. She died at Alessandria in
1590.

Christina was often painted and several portraits still exist. As a very
young child she appears in the group of Christian II's three children, by
Gossaert.[2] As Duchess of Milan she was painted by van Orley and by
Titian.[3] In 1538, a few days before Holbein reached Brussels, she was
painted out of mourning by a court painter.[4] A drawing of her is preserved in the Recueil d'Arras.[5] Probable or possible portraits of 1545 and
1549 are known[6]; another is dated 1558.[7] A posthumous(?) portrait with
her daughter-in-law and granddaughter is in the Prado.[8]

The circumstances surrounding the origin of No. 2475 are of course connected with Henry VIII's attempt to marry the sitter.[9] The English Ambassador at Brussels, John Hutton, managed first to obtain the Flemish painter's portrait of Christina which he despatched to England on 9 March 1538. The following day Holbein, accompanied by Philip Hoby, unexpectedly arrived for the purpose of recording Christina's features. The ambassador stopped despatch of the first portrait since 'it was not soo perffight as the cawse requyrid, neyther as the said Mr Haunce coold make it.'[10] On 12 March Christina sat to Holbein for 'thre owers space' and the ambassador found the result 'very perffight'.[11] It is not clear whether this was a drawing or perhaps, more likely, a painting on parchment comparable to the *Anne of Cleves* (Louvre),[12] itself done on a similar occasion.

From this drawing or painting Holbein is likely to have evolved No. 2475, probably soon after the Brussels visit. Christina did not sit to him again; he was back in England on 18 March and a day or two later the king had seen with pleasure the likeness taken at Brussels.[13] It is reasonable to suppose No. 2475 was painted in 1538, during the later part of which year Holbein was out of England (partly in connection with recording other candidates for Henry's marriage). Nothing is known of the purpose of No. 2475 and there are no contemporary mentions of it.

It need not be doubted that Christina appears in No. 2475 in mourning. The English ambassador's earliest reference to having seen her says that she wears mourning after the Italian fashion, and the Flemish portrait already mentioned is explicitly said to show her out of mourning (implying an exception). Christina was remarked on for her height and Brantôme records the beauty of her hands which were praised by Catherine de' Medici,[14] herself the possessor of the most beautiful hand 'qui fut jamais veue'.

The *cartellino* on No. 2475 is clearly not by Holbein nor contemporary with him. Other portraits, not always by Holbein, which were in the Lumley collection bear similar sorts of label, and No. 2475 was almost certainly in the same collection. The label was therefore very probably added at that time.[15]

VERSIONS AND COPIES: A three-quarter length which has been attributed to Holbein's studio, in the Earl of Stamford's collection.[16] That picture or another in the Sykes sale, 1733–4.[17] A Flemish(?) half length is at Windsor.[18] A full-length copy in Mrs. R. ffennell sale, London, 5 October 1956 (lot 28).[19] A drawing by van Dyck seems to be after No. 2475.[20]

PROVENANCE: Old inventories do not of course distinguish between the original and any copies that may have existed; but the following entries (except when marked as doubtful) apparently refer to the National Gallery picture. A full length of the sitter was in the inventories of Henry VIII of 24 April 1542; and 1547 (no. 12).[21] What is almost certainly the same picture is referred to in the audit of the accounts of Sir Anthony Denny, Keeper of the Palace of Westminster, in February 1551; it is said to have been given by the King (meaning Henry VIII) to (Henry Fitzalan) Earl of Arundel (died 1580), who presumably made good his claim.[22] Said, very probably in error, to have been seen by Zucchero at the Earl of Pembroke's *ca.* 1574.[23] The National Gallery picture in all probability appears in the 1590 inventory of John, 7th Lord Lumley, who is likely to have inherited it (together with Nonsuch Palace) from Henry Fitzalan (his first wife's father) in 1580[24]; Lord Lumley died in 1609, and this picture probably remained in London in the possession of his widow by a second marriage until her death in 1617, at which time it might have been bequeathed to her brother, Thomas, 3rd Lord Darcy.[25] A *Christina* was in a Lumley sale, 1785, fetching £7 10s., but this was presumably only a copy; for what is clearly the original was seen by Sandrart in 1627 in London(?), in the possession of Thomas Howard, Earl of Arundel,[26] who was the great-nephew of the 7th Lord Lumley, and obtained several of his pictures, but apparently not by bequest. The Arundel picture was removed to Holland (probably in 1643), and was in the inventory after death at Amsterdam of Thomas Howard's widow, Aletheia, who died in 1654.[27] At the time of this inventory, the only surviving son was William, Lord Stafford (1614–1680), who claimed all the pictures[28]; it seems clear that he had No. 2475 at least, for it was owned by his son, created Earl of Stafford (1648–1719), in whose Gallery at Tart Hall or Stafford House, London (also inherited from his father) it was seen by Vertue in 1720.[29] This picture was not in the Stafford House sale of 1720, but passed to Lord Stafford's cousin and executor, Mr. Howard of Greystoke[30]; *i.e.* Henry Charles, who died in 1730, and then to his son Charles, in whose house in Soho Square it was seen by Vertue *ca.* 1744(?). Vertue says it was after that removed to Greystoke Castle, but by 1768 it was at Worksop Manor[31]; this was one of the seats of the Dukes of Norfolk, and the Charles Howard just mentioned did become the 10th Duke of Norfolk, but this was only in 1777, in succession to his first cousin once removed. There is therefore a doubt about the provenance at this point; but it may be noted that old Worksop Manor (inherited from the father of the 8th and 9th Dukes) with most of its contents was destroyed by fire in 1761, so that the transference there of No. 2475 may have taken place on the furnishing of the new house, although Charles Howard did not become heir presumptive to the 9th Duke until February, 1767. Still at Worksop Manor in 1813[32]; the house was sold in 1840[33] and the picture was (perhaps at that time) transferred to Arundel Castle, where seen by Waagen.[34] Lent by the Duke of Norfolk to the National Gallery, 1880–1909, except when sent for exhibition at the Royal Academy, 1880 (no. 177), at the New Gallery (Tudor), 1890 (no. 92), at the Grafton Gallery (Fair Women), 1894 (no. 4), and at Manchester (Royal House of Tudor), 1897 (no. 47). Sold in 1909 by the 15th Duke of Norfolk to Colnaghi's; purchased from them by the National Art-Collections Fund, with the aid of a special Treasury grant and a large anonymous donation, and presented, 1909. Exhibited National Art-Collections Fund exhibition, National Gallery, 1945–6 (no. 24).

REPRODUCTION: *Illustrations, Continental Schools*, 1937, p. 165.

REFERENCES: (1) For her biography in detail, see Julia Cartwright, *Christina of Denmark, Duchess of Milan and Lorraine*, 1913, whence most of the following facts have been taken. (2) Versions at Hampton Court (recorded in Henry VIII inventory of 1542) and in the Earl of Radnor collection, among others; cf. the exhibition catalogue *Flemish Art 1300–1700*, Royal Academy, 1953–4, nos. 54 and 56. (3) Van Orley's portrait was full-length and is recorded as paid for in Mary of Hungary's accounts of 1533: cf. A. Pinchart in *Revue Universelle des Arts*, III, 1856, p. 142, note 2. The Titian portrait is recorded in her inventory, Pinchart, *loc. cit.*, p. 140 (no. 7); see further J. A. Crowe and G. B. Cavalcaselle, *Titian*, 1877, I, p. 355, cited and commented on by Cartwright, *op. cit.*, p. 96. (4) Cartwright, *op. cit.*, p. 154. Her tacit assumption that Bernaert van Orley was the painter is misleading (for there seems no evidence); he was not the sole court painter, as Scrots had been appointed in 1537. That this picture was by van Orley is also stated by J. de Jongh, *Mary of Hungary* (English ed.) 1959, p. 184. What has sometimes been supposed to be this picture is a half-length at Windsor (see under Versions). (5) Photo Giraudon, 11730. (6) See G. Glück in Vienna *Jahrbuch*, 1934, pp. 188–90. (7) Attributed to François Clouet; cf.

the exhibition catalogue, *Chefs-d'œuvre de l'Art Français*, Paris, 1937, no. 41, recording a drawing for it in the British Museum, a copy at Besançon and a miniature in the Uffizi. (8) *Museo del Prado: Catalogo* ..., 1949, pp. 783–4 (no. 1951). (9) See especially the discussion in A. B. Chamberlain, *Hans Holbein the Younger*, 1913, II, pp. 114 ff. (10) Chamberlain, *op. cit.*, p. 121. Cartwright, *op. cit.*, p. 155, says the ambassador failed to stop the first picture leaving, but the sense of the letter printed in full by Chamberlain is against that. (11) Chamberlain, *op. cit.*, p. 123. (12) Verbal suggestion kindly made to the present writer by David Piper. (13) Chamberlain, *op. cit.*, p. 124. (14) Cf. *Œuvres*, 1823, V, p. 319. (15) See the discussion by David Piper in *The Burlington Magazine*, XCIX, 1957, pp. 224 ff. (p. 227 for No. 2475). (16) See the exhibition catalogue, *Works by Holbein and other Masters*, Royal Academy, 1950–1, no. 22. (17) See Vertue's note published by The Walpole Society, vol. XXIV (1935–6) p. 51. (18) *Holbein* ... exhibition R.A. (1950–1 (no. 23) as after Holbein. The picture was published by G. Ring in *The Burlington Magazine*, XCIII, 1951, pp. 88 ff., as a work of the 'Regent Master' whose name had also been mentioned in connection with it by Friedländer. She attempts to identify it with the picture of Christina which Hutton obtained before Holbein reached Brussels. This attempt had already been made by Cartwright, *op. cit.*, p. 158, note 1. However, there is at least one serious objection: in that first portrait Christina, according to Hutton's confidante, was shown out of mourning. Ring's attempts to interpret this statement so as to fit with the Windsor portrait (where there is full mourning) are peculiarly unconvincing. (19) Inscribed as Katherine, 4th wife of Charles Brandon, Duke of Suffolk. (20) Published by O. Fischel in *Old Master Drawings*, Sept. 1933, p. 22 and pl. 25, and dated 1620–1. The closeness to No. 2475 is slight. (21) Chamberlain, *op. cit.*, II, p. 129. These facts are also given in P. Ganz, *The Paintings of Hans Holbein*, 1950, p. 249 (no. 98) where further provenance is given wrongly. (22) This information supplied from a Lansdowne Roll (no. 15) in a letter of 1924 from J. P. Gilson, in the Gallery archives. (23) C. van Mander, *Het Schilder-Boeck*, 1604, f. 223 recto. (24) See The Walpole Society, vol. VI (1917–18), p. 21; also Piper, *loc. cit.*, p. 224. (25) Cf. Mary F. S. Hervey, *The Life of Thomas Howard, Earl of Arundel*, 1921, pp. 52 ff. (26) *Lebenslauf* ... *Joachims von Sandrart*, 1675, p. 6, at the end of *Die Teutsche Akademie*, II Theil. (27) Hervey, *op. cit.*, pp. 473 and 482 (no. 193); Mary L. Cox in *The Burlington Magazine*, XIX, 1911, p. 282. (28) According to Hervey, *op. cit.*, p. 410, Lord Stafford actually obtained all the pictures in the Amsterdam inventory. (29) Vertue in The Walpole Society, vol. XVIII (1929–30), p. 65 and vol. XXVI (1937–8), pp. 26–7. (30) Vertue in The Walpole Society, vol. XX (1931–2), pp. 83–4 and vol. XXVI (1937–8), p. 31. (31) Walpole's note, 1768, in The Walpole Society, vol. XVI (1927–8), pp. 65–6. (32) *Beauties of England and Wales*, XII (Notts), 1813, p. 344. (33) For the destruction of the earlier Worksop Manor, and sale of the house in 1840, see Murray's *Handbook for Derbyshire, Nottinghamshire* ..., 1892–1904 ed., p. 97. (34) Waagen, *Treasures of Art* ..., 1854, III, p. 29.

Johann LISS
ca. 1595?–1629/30

Occasionally also *Lys*.[1] The date of birth is not known, nor the place. Liss was from Holstein on the evidence of his own inscriptions; Sandrart (the sole other authority) records him as from the Oldenburg region.[2] His parents have been rather doubtfully identified by Steinbart[3] with a pair of painters, Johann and Anna Liss (or Lissen) recorded as active in the Oldenburg region in the first half of the seventeenth century. Sandrart says nothing of his early training except that Liss went to Amsterdam to form a *Heinrich Golzii Manier*, and thence passed to Paris, Venice and Rome.[4] An inscribed drawing records him in Venice in 1621[5]; another records him at Rome on 19 March 16.. (the last figures lacking).[6] He was a member of the Netherlandish painters' club at Rome, the Bent, and was nicknamed *Pan*. He is listed in the *fraglia* of Venetian painters only in 1629. He died at Venice from plague, 1629 or 1630.

Liss painted chiefly genre and religious pictures. A chronology can be, and has been, deduced from the various influences on him; there are in effect no dated pictures and very few signed.[7] The *Inspiration of S. Jerome* painted for S. Niccolò dei Tolentini, Venice (and still *in situ*), was apparently seen by Sandrart when at Venice, 1628–9.

REFERENCES: *General:* K. Steinbart, *Johann Liss*, 1940; and the same author and title, 1946 (a different and less detailed book).
In text: (1) Cf. for instance A. Welcker in *Oud-Holland*, 1947, pp. 135–6, reproducing a drawing so signed. (2) Cf. A. Peltzer's ed. of the *Academie*, 1925, pp. 187–8. (3) *Johann Liss*, 1940, p. 5. (4) Since Sandrart knew Liss and gives a vivid picture of him and his work, it might be thought odd that he omitted the fact (if it was one) that both his parents were painters—an unusual enough fact in itself. (5) In the Kunsthalle, Hamburg; signed: *Johan Liss Holsacia. A. 1621 | a VEN*; Steinbart, *op. cit.*, 1940, pl. 4. (6) Steinbart, *ib.*, *pl.* 30; it is now in the Cleveland Museum. (7) A signed and dated *Agony in the Garden* (Steinbart, *ib.*, pl. 49): *Ioañes: Liss: F. | A:D: 162..* The last figure has been read as a 9; Steinbart apparently accepts this with a query.

4597 JUDITH IN THE TENT OF HOLOFERNES

Judith is handing Holofernes' head to her Negro maid.
Canvas, 50⅝ × 39 (1·285 × 0·99).
In good condition under engrained varnish.

The subject is from the apocryphal *Book of Judith*, xiii, 8–10. No. 4597 was ascribed to Fetti until it was correctly attributed by Oldenbourg.[1] The composition exists in more than one version, though not all of these are convincingly from the hand of Liss himself. As prototype for the figures of Judith and her maid, Steinbart has claimed a Pordenone of the same subject in the Galleria Borghese, Rome, and there is some similarity[2]; he therefore puts the earliest version *ca.* 1622–3 after Liss had returned to Venice from Rome.

Steinbart's evolution for the various versions seems partly invalidated by examination of them.[3] Thus the rectangular version at Ca' Rezzonico, Venice, claimed by him as the earliest on account of the format, is in fact an upright picture which (at a later date?) has been expanded by the addition of the scene at the right[4]; even allowing for this it may be doubted if the original upright picture there is by Liss himself. The status of other versions does not however affect No. 4597 for which Steinbart has proposed a date 1625–6[5]; this is probably the latest period for its execution and, judging from its tenebrist lighting, it could well date from a year or two earlier.

The composition was engraved by Pietro Monaco in 1739 when a

version was in the Vidmani (Weidmann) collection at Venice.[6] A version
of good quality at Budapest (see below further) has been claimed to be
that picture, but confirmation seems lacking and the point cannot be
decided in the absence of further evidence.

ENGRAVING : An engraving of the design by Monaco has been mentioned
above.

VERSIONS AND COPIES : A repetition is at Budapest[7]; another (not auto-
graph ?) is at Vienna,[8] a third is in a private collection at Venice.[9] A rectangular
version in Ca' Rezzonico, Venice, has been mentioned above. A copy of the
upper half of the composition was in an anonymous sale, London, 5 May 1937
(lot 61).[10]

PROVENANCE : By 1914 in the collection of Prof. Naager, Munich,[11] and lent
by him to the Alte Pinakothek until 1919 when purchased for James W. Dollar,
by whom presented, 1931.

REPRODUCTIONS : *Illustrations, Italian Schools*, 1937, p. 205; *Illustrations,
Continental Schools*, 1937, p. 197.

REFERENCES : (1) R. Oldenbourg in the Prussian *Jahrbuch*, 1914, p. 150.
(2) The Borghese picture is reproduced by Steinbart, *op. cit.*, 1940, fig. 54.
This picture seems first recorded in the inventory of Olimpia Aldobrandini
(1682) as by Titian; cf. P. della Pergola, *Galleria Borghese*: I, *I Dipinti*, 1955,
p. 126. Liss would probably pay more attention to it under that attribution
than under its present attribution. (3) *Op. cit.*, pp. 119 ff., for his discussion.
(4) Reproduced by Steinbart, *op. cit.*, 1940, pl. 45 (then at Palazzo Vendramin-
Calergi). (5) *Op. cit.*, p. 159. (6) The engraving (dated) is pl. 4 of Vol. I, *Raccolta
di Centododici Stampe di Pitture della Storia Sacra*, 1763. (7) Budapest *Catalogue*,
1954, pp. 338–9, with bibliography. (8) Vienna *Catalogue*, 1938, no. 1244A,
without provenance. The picture is apparently first recorded in an inventory
of 1870 as by an unknown painter and as a copy, and to have previously been
in the Residenz at Salzburg (letter of 1954 from Dr. Klauner in the Gallery
archives). (9) Steinbart, *op. cit.*, 1940, pl. 46, when in the Italico Brass collection; this picture was included in the exhibition, *De Venetiaanse Meesters*,
Amsterdam, 1953 (no. 53), with previous exhibition references. (10) As by
Spada, *Salome with the head of John the Baptist*, according to a note in the
Gallery archives. (11) When published by Oldenbourg, *loc. cit.*, in the note 1
above.

STEPHAN LOCHNER
Active 1442–died 1451

Probably born at Meersburg[1] on Lake Constance, at a date not
known. He is first recorded in June 1442 at Cologne, when he was paid
for various decorations in connection with the visit to the city of the
Emperor Frederick III.[2] There are further references to him at Cologne
until 1451; in 1447 he was elected a councillor of the painters' guild, and
again served in 1450. It can be deduced that he was still alive on 22
September 1451, when permission was sought during an outbreak of
plague for a new graveyard to be made adjoining Lochner's house.[3] By
Christmas 1451 he was dead.[4]

There are no signed pictures and it seems that no contracts for pictures have survived. Attributions are based on the *Adoration of the Kings*

triptych for the chapel of the town hall, Cologne (now in the Cathedral); it was seen in 1520 by Dürer who records it as by 'maister Steffan zu Cöln'.[5] A *Presentation in the Temple* (Gulbenkian collection) is dated 1445 [6]; a very much more elaborate picture of the same subject (at Darmstadt) is dated 1447.

REFERENCES : *General*: O. Förster, *Stefan Lochner*, 1938.

In text: (1) A letter of 16 August 1451 from the town council of Cologne to the Meersburg council mentions the recent death of Lochner's parents at Meersburg and the painter's inability (through illness?) at that time to travel to Meersburg: published first by J. J. Merlo, *Kölnische Künstler in alter und neuer Zeit* (ed. E. Firmenich-Richartz and H. Keussen) 1895, cols. 836–7. (2) Published first by B. Kuske, *Zeitschrift für christliche Kunst*, 1908, cols. 89–90. The reference does not occur in H. Schrade, *Stephan Lochner*, 1923, and is given in error as July 1442 by O. Förster in Thieme-Becker *Lexikon*, XXIII, *ad vocem*. (3) Merlo, *op. cit.*, cols. 834–5. (4) His name marked with a cross in the list of councillors for 1450–1 (the period of office ran from Christmas Day to Christmas Day): Merlo, *op. cit.*, col. 832. (5) In his Netherlands diary; cf. the edition of J. Veth and S. Muller, 1918, I, p. 65. (6) Published by L. Baldass, *Wallraf-Richartz Jahrbuch*, 1933–4, pp. 233 ff. wrongly as dated 1447; corrected by A. Stange in *Deutsche Malerei der Gotik*, III: *Norddeutschland in der Zeit von 1400 bis 1450*, 1938, p. 95.

705   SS. MATTHEW, CATHERINE OF ALEXANDRIA AND JOHN THE EVANGELIST

Verso: S. Jerome, a female martyr, S. Gregory the Great, and a kneeling donor in the cloak of a Knight of Malta. S. Gregory's book with paragraphs beginning: $O \mid N \mid I \mid A \mid Q$.[1]

Oak, $27 \times 22\frac{7}{8}$ (0·686 × 0·581); cut down at top and bottom.

The *recto* is in quite good condition under discoloured varnish, though the gold is new. The *verso* is very considerably damaged and abraded; complete paint losses amount to more than half the area.

S. Matthew is accompanied by his angel; S. Catherine is shown crowned, holding a sword and with fragments of her wheel at her feet; S. John holds a chalice with a serpent and is accompanied by a haloed eagle. S. Jerome is shown as a cardinal; remains of the Dove at S. Gregory's ear.

The female martyr on the *verso* holds a palm and there are slight traces of a crown about her head. Originally she was identified as S. Ursula but in the 1929 catalogue was called, with a query, S. Catherine. It is quite clear that S. Catherine would not appear twice on the same wing. Possibly S. Ursula is intended, though she is usually shown with a book or with an arrow. In view of the provenance of No. 705, for which see further below, it would not be unlikely that the figure here is for S. Cordula. She was one of the virgins who accompanied S. Ursula to Cologne but, taking fright, she hid in the bottom of the boat and only later emerged for martyrdom. Her appearances in art are rare but she does usually wear a crown and, though her attribute is a ship, apparently at times has no other distinguishing symbol except her palm.[2]

No. 705 is the left-hand wing of an altarpiece, the right-hand wing of which (*recto* and *verso* separated) is in the Wallraf-Richartz Museum, Cologne.[3] The present *verso* of No. 705 was the outside, and together the outside wings showed the four Fathers of the Church, the unidentified female martyr and S. Cecilia(?)[4] in an architectural setting, with two kneeling donors in the dress of Knights of Malta; the inside wings showed the four Evangelists with SS. Catherine and Barbara. The donor on the relevant Cologne panel has his name inscribed below: *Fr. heynricus zeuwelgyn. laycus*; on No. 705 this portion of the panel has been cut away.

At one time the dress of the donors was mistakenly supposed to be that of the Teutonic order[5] and the pictures were then said to come from the church of the Order at Cologne, S. Catherine's. The church of the Order of S. John of Jerusalem was SS. John and Cordula[6] and presumably the pictures came from there, though the point does not seem fully established. Nothing is known of whether there was a central panel of the altarpiece; conceivably there was a sculpted central feature and not a picture.

The correct attribution of No. 705 was made by Waagen.[7] The suggestion of Reiners that these wings are the work of pupils is not at all borne out by examination and his association of them with the two von Pannwitz (now van Beuningen) pictures is misleading.[8] Equally misleading is the comment of Förster on their condition and the probable intervention of the studio.[9] The present *recto* of No. 705 is perfectly acceptable as Lochner's own work and its high quality is obscured only by discoloured varnish.

Stange has stylistically associated the London/Cologne wings with a *Crucifixion with Saints* (at Nuremberg) which there is some reason for supposing may date from *ca.* 1440.[10] Lochner's chronology is confused and puzzling; thus the Gulbenkian picture of 1445 (there seems no reason to doubt the last figure) is in a less developed style than No. 705 which has affinities with the Nuremberg *Crucifixion*. Baldass, noting the affinity, apparently tends to date No. 705 after the *Crucifixion*[11] and the present writer thinks No. 705 slightly more developed in style and arguably therefore of rather later date.

PROVENANCE: Presumably from the church of SS. John and Cordula, Cologne, as mentioned above. Acquired from the Cologne dealer, Dethier, by the brothers Sulpiz and Melchior Boisserée and exchanged by them in 1814, for another picture, with Count Joseph von Rechberg.[12] Acquired thence by Prince Ludwig Kraft Ernst von Oettingen-Wallerstein; at Schloss Wallerstein.[13] Exhibited for sale at Kensington Palace, 1848 (No. 51), bought with the rest of the collection by the Prince Consort; at Kensington Palace, 1854.[14] Presented by Queen Victoria, at the Prince Consort's wish, 1863.

REPRODUCTION: *Illustrations, Continental Schools*, 1937, p. 194 (*recto* and *verso*).

REFERENCES: (1) It is perhaps worth noting that the column to the left of S. Gregory has its capital ornamented by what in reproduction looks rather like a date. Examination shows that these hooks and strokes are intended as decoration and have no other significance. (2) See J. Braun, *Tracht und Attribute der*

Heiligen in der deutschen Kunst, 1943, cols. 436–7 and K. Künstle, *Ikonographie der christlichen Kunst*, II, 1926, p. 169. (3) Cf. the reproductions in O. Förster, *Stefan Lochner*, 1938, pl. 20. (4) Cologne 1957 catalogue, for example, without a query; but it does not seem quite sure that the saint is S. Cecilia. (5) Presumably for this reason, the SS. John and Cordula provenance proposed by Merlo, *Die Meister der Altkölnischen Malerschule*, 1852, p. 126, was explicitly altered in *Kölnische Künstler* . . . ed. E. Firmenich-Richartz and H. Keussen, 1895, col. 848, note 4. The correct(?) provenance stated again by E. Firmenich-Richartz in *Zeitschrift für christliche Kunst*, 1893, cols. 204–5. The wrong provenance repeated by O. Förster, *op. cit.*, p. 155. (6) See for example P. Hélyot, *Histoire des Ordres Monastiques, Religieux et Militaires*, III, 1715, p. 116: cited by M. Davies in *Paintings and Drawings on the Backs of National Gallery Pictures*, 1946, p. 9, where the *verso* of No. 705 is discussed (illustrated, pl. 15). (7) *Descriptive Catalogue of a collection of . . . pictures now in Kensington Palace*, 1854, pp. 15–16. (8) H. Reiners, *Die Kölner Malerschule*, 1925, p. 91. In passing, it may be noted that there are no grounds for the dogmatic assertion of F. W. Lippmann that No. 705 is 'distinctly a work of Lochner's contemporary, the Master of the Heisterbach altar'; see his letter in *The Burlington Magazine*, XII, 1907–8, p. 108. (9) Förster, *loc. cit.* (10) *Deutsche Malerei der Gotik*, III: *Norddeutschland in der Zeit von 1400 bis 1450*, 1938, p. 105, with discussion of the dating of the Nuremberg *Crucifixion*. (11) See L. Baldass in *Wallraf-Richartz Jahrbuch*, 1933–4, pp. 233 ff. (12) For these facts see E. Firmenich-Richartz, *Die Brüder Boisserée*, vol. I, 1916, pp. 248 and 482; the picture they obtained was part of an altarpiece by Strigel. (13) In the 1826(?) lithographed catalogue and 1827 MS. catalogue (originals at Munich; photostats in National Gallery) no. 60 as Master Wilhelm. Marked in the MS. catalogue as ex-Boisserée. For some comment on the formation of the collection in general see G. Grupp in *Jahrbuch des historischen Vereins für Nördlingen und Umgebung*, VI, 1917, pp. 73 ff. (14) Waagen's catalogue, no. 22; see note 7.

JOHANN CARL LOTH
1632–1698

In Italy often called *Carlotto*. Born at Munich, 8 August 1632,[1] son of the painter, Johann Ulrich Loth, under whom probably trained. Possibly he worked for a period in Rome. He settled in Venice at least by 1660 [2] and was much influenced by earlier Venetian art and by his contemporaries, among them Pietro Liberi. Nicodemus Tessin records in some detail a visit in 1687 to Loth at Venice[3]; there are otherwise few contemporary mentions. He died at Venice, 6 October 1698, and is said on his funerary tablet[4] to have been ennobled by the Emperor Leopold.

There are apparently no signed or dated works, but the S. Silvestro altarpiece (Venice) has recently been established as of 1681.[5] Some other pictures in Venetian churches are recorded as his and Zanetti gives a list of them.[6] Loth also painted altarpieces for Munich. Apart from religious pictures, he produced chiefly pictures of mythological and historical subjects.[7] A number of South German baroque painters trained in his studio.

REFERENCES: (1) For this and further see Nasse's entry in Thieme-Becker *Lexikon*, XXIII, *ad vocem*. (2) Boschini, *La Carta del Nauegar Pitoresco*, 1660, p. 554. (3) *Studieresor* (ed. O. Sirén) 1914, p. 203. (4) In S. Luca, Venice; the inscription given in full by A. M. Zanetti, *Della Pittura Veneziana*, 1771, p. 522, note. (5) By G. Ewald; for references see under No. 187 in the exhibition catalogue, *La Pittura del Seicento a Venezia*, Venice, 1959, p. 118. (6) *Op. cit.*, pp. 522–3. (7) For some attributions, see H. Voss in *Zeitschrift für bildende Kunst*, 1912, pp. 69 ff.

3571 MERCURY PIPING TO ARGUS

At the left the head of Io transformed into a white heifer.

Canvas, 46 × 39¼ (1·169 × 0·997); slightly cut down at the left.

In good condition; there are some damages and repaint in the heifer's head and in the index finger of Argus.

The story of Io, loved by Jupiter and transformed by him into a heifer to avoid Juno's jealousy, is of extreme antiquity. Juno, discovering the heifer's identity, had it guarded by Argus Panoptes. Mercury was sent by Jupiter to kill Argus, which he did. The incident of Mercury piping Argus asleep seems not to occur in literature before Ovid, *Metamorphoses*, i, and just possibly Ovid invented it.

No. 3571 has previously been catalogued as by Liss, but Fiocco long ago pointed out the correct painter.[1] The style seems not far from *Apollo and Jupiter in the house of Philemon and Baucis* (at Vienna)[2] and that picture is pre-1659.[3]

PROVENANCE: Presented by A. G. H. Ward, through the National Art-Collections Fund, 1920.

REPRODUCTION: *Illustrations, Continental Schools*, 1937, p. 197.

REFERENCES: (1) G. Fiocco, *Venetian Painting of the Seicento and the Settecento*, 1929, p. 43. (2) Reproduced by Voss, *op. cit.*, p. 70. (3) When recorded in the Archduke Leopold William inventory.

MASTER OF THE AACHEN ALTARPIECE
Active late XV–early XVI century

He is named from a *Crucifixion* altarpiece now in the Cathedral treasury at Aachen, but during the nineteenth century in the Lyversberg collection and almost certainly from a church at Cologne. Cologne seems the place of the Master's activity, whatever his place of birth. The personality is the creation of Friedländer[1] out of a group of pictures, some of which were previously classed with the Master of S. Severin; a fresco of the *Raising of Lazarus* in S. Maria im Kapitol, Cologne, was also attributed to him by Friedländer. All these pictures show affinities with the work of the younger Master of the Holy Kindred, and especially with the Master of S. Severin and the Master of S. Ursula (*q.v.*). So close are the affinities that it is far from clear if all the pictures attributed to the Aachen Master are really by the same hand.[2] For the purposes of this entry, it is sufficient to say that No. 1049 below (and its wings at Liverpool) seem to the present writer quite certainly by the same hand as that of the Aachen altarpiece.

REFERENCES: (1) See his article in *Wallraf-Richartz Jahrbuch*, 1924, pp. 101 ff. (2) The personality is rejected by H. Brockmann, *Die Spätzeit der Kölner*

Malerschule, 1924, pp. 227 ff., but is accepted and expanded by H. Reiners, *Die Kölner Malerschule*, 1925, pp. 231 ff. There is firm acceptance of him as a personality in A. Stange, *Deutsche Malerei* . . . V: *Köln in der Zeit von 1450 bis 1515*, 1952, pp. 115 ff.

1049 THE CRUCIFIXION

Christ on the Cross, between the Virgin and S. John; left, three holy women mourning. In the left background Christ falls under the Cross on his way to Calvary; right background Christ is taken down from the Cross. Right foreground, soldiers dicing. Traces of gold lettering along the edges of the Virgin's robe; on the fold about her head: *STABAT MATRE*; on the skirt: *QUIS·(E)ST · HOM | VI · NON · FLE | MATREM · CRISTI · S(I?) VI(D) | IN · TANTO · SU(P)*

Oak, painted area, 42¼ × 47⅜ (1·073 × 1·203).

Good condition in general. There is very slight wearing in a few places and a damage in S. John's hair and left shoulder. The gold haloes and lettering are slightly worn; originally the other edges of the Virgin's robe were also lettered.

The words on the Virgin's robe are from the sequence *Stabat Mater*, used in the Mass for the feast of the Seven Dolours but for long a popular hymn. In the Roman Missal, verse 3: *Quis est homo, qui non fleret | Matrem Christi si videret | In tanto supplicio?*[1] The verse was perhaps completed along the upper edge of the Virgin's robe, but the lettering there is no longer decipherable.

No. 1049 is the central panel of a triptych of which the wings are at Liverpool; they show *Christ before Pilate* and the *Deposition*. The complete altarpiece is thus analogous with the Master's triptych at Aachen, after which he is named; the treatment of the Crucifixion in both altarpieces seems based to some extent on that of the Master of the Holy Kindred.[2]

Friedländer, to whom the attribution and the connection of the pictures is due,[3] placed the London/Liverpool altarpiece rather earlier in date than the Aachen picture, on the grounds that the more contorted restless forms of the latter show it to be later.[4] Stange accepts this chronology[5] which is also based in part on the varying appearance of a face in pictures by the Master, supposed by Friedländer to be a self-portrait. The latter grounds seem dangerously subjective. The present writer thinks the handling of the altarpiece under discussion quite close to the Aachen triptych, and there is probably no good reason to suppose the two altarpieces separated by any considerable gap in time.[6]

PROVENANCE: Recorded as having been brought from Flanders to England at the time of the French Revolution.[7] Apparently later with an art dealer at Manchester, from whom bought by a Mr. Dixon, a merchant of Newcastle. Bought from his executors by Edward Shipperdson, by whom presented, 1847.[8]

REPRODUCTION: *Illustrations, Continental Schools*, 1937, p. 210.

REFERENCES : (1) For some discussion of the sequence and quotation of the two chief versions, cf. H. A. Daniel, *Thesaurus Hymnologicus*, I, 1851, pp. 131 ff. (2) Compare the *Crucifixion* at Brussels by the Master of the Holy Kindred; for the point, see Stange, *Deutsche Malerei der Gotik*, V, 1952, p. 116. (3) See his review of the New Gallery exhibition of 1900 in *Repertorium für Kunstwissenschaft*, 1900, p. 258; also C. Aldenhoven, *Geschichte der Kölner Malerschule*, 1902, p. 291. Some further comment is in H. Brockmann, *Die Spätzeit der Kölner Malerschule*, 1924, pp. 229–30. (4) *Wallraf-Richartz Jahrbuch*, 1924, p. 102. (5) *Op. cit.*, p. 118. (6) Michael Compton, who is cataloguing the Liverpool wings, has independently reached the conclusion that the two triptychs are close together in date. (7) Letter of 1847 from E. Shipperdson in the Gallery archives; the remainder of the provenance is derived from this. It is not clear whether the wings of the altarpiece had already been separated from No. 1049 before its arrival in England. (8) As German School: the names of Aldegrever and, inevitably, Dürer being mentioned as possible authors. In the National Gallery catalogue of 1898 as Westphalian(?) School, XVth century.

MASTER OF CAPPENBERG
Active early XVI century

He is named after a *Crucifixion* altarpiece at Cappenberg (Kappenberg).[1] The pictures associated with him are Westphalian; none is signed or dated but all seem to date approximately from the first quarter of the sixteenth century. They include a series of fourteen pictures of the Virgin's Life and Christ's Passion (now in the Landesmuseum, Münster) and portions of a *S. Anthony* altarpiece in S. Victor's, Xanten.[2] An important scattered series of pictures, by the same hand, includes Nos. 263 and 2154 catalogued below.

All these works show a close relationship to Derick Baegert[3] (active at his birthplace, Wesel, and elsewhere in Westphalia; not recorded later than 1515). F. Witte[4] was the first to suggest that the Cappenberg master was in fact his son, Jan Baegert, whose activity chiefly as a craftsman but also as a painter is documented. More recently, A. Stange[5] has put forward what seems a very convincing case for linking the series, of which the two pictures below are part, with the two wings of the Liesborn high altar for which Jan Baegert was paid in 1520 (the single documented instance at present of his activity as a painter[6]). If this series could definitely be shown to come from Liesborn, Stange's identification would be strongly supported. But the exact provenance of these pictures is not established, and some other points which are discussed below increase the uncertainty.

The evidence therefore does not yet seem firm enough to justify altering the previously accepted heading above, even while it may be admitted that Jan Baegert probably *is* the Cappenberg master.[7] In any event, the nucleus of pictures associated with this hand remains the same.

REFERENCES : (1) See L. Scheibler in Prussian *Jahrbuch*, 1882, pp. 27–8. At that time and later the influence on him of the Dünwege brothers was supposed (cf. W. Kaesbach, *Das Werk der Maler Viktor und Heinrich Duenwege und des Meisters von Kappenberg*, 1907) since they were erroneously held responsible

for work really by Derick Baegert. (2) For these pictures, with others attributed
to the Cappenberg Master, see the exhibition catalogue *Der Maler Derick
Baegert und sein Kreis*, Münster, Sept. 1937, nos. 54–86. (3) For whom cf.
A. Sprung, *Derick Baegert aus Wesel . . .* 1937. (4) In *Zeitschrift des rheinischen
Vereins für Denkmalpflege und Heimatschutz*, 1931, (2), pp. 85 ff. To avoid
inevitable confusion, it should perhaps be added that though some numbers of
the *Zeitschrift* were also issued as volumes of the *Jahrbuch der rheinischen Denkmalpflege*, the relevant number (a *Jubiläumsheft*) was not. See also F. Witte in
Tausend Jahre deutscher Kunst am Rhein, 1932, I, pp. 151 ff.; for the documented
dates of his activity, see the same writer, *op. cit.*, V (*Quellen zur rheinischen
Kunstgeschichte*), p. 134. (5) In *Westfalen*, 1952, pp. 198 ff. (6) A group of documents was first published by A. Wormstall in *Zeitschrift für vaterländische
Geschichte und Altertumskunde Westfalens*, 1897, pp. 87 ff. For some cautionary
comments on which references are undoubtedly to Baegert, see Rensing in
Westfalen, 1937, pp. 247–8. The relevant notices for Baegert, including the
specific mention of 1520: 'Pro duabus alis tabule summi altaris/ Post Ascensionis
domini magistro Johanni Baghert. . . .', given again in Stange, *op. cit.*, p. 198.
(7) The identification is sustained by G. van Oyen, *Jan Baegert: der Meister
von Cappenberg*, 1953 (unpublished dissertation): relevant portions for Nos. 263
and 2154 catalogued below were kindly presented by the author to the Gallery.

263   THE CORONATION OF THE VIRGIN

The Virgin's halo inscribed: *sancta. maria.*

Oak, $38\frac{1}{4} \times 27\frac{3}{4}$ (0·972 × 0·705), painted up to the edges all round,
including narrow borders of brown and red paint at the top and left-hand
side. Almost certainly cut at the bottom.

In quite good condition under discoloured varnish. A large crack
running perpendicularly up through the Virgin's cloak and dress,
Christ's knee and the left-hand portion of the Virgin's halo; along this
area is clumsy repainting. The gold of the haloes of Christ and God the
Father is damaged in places and repainted.

The subject, though popular, is not based on any specific text.
Certain Old Testament references, as that in I *Kings*, ii, 19, where
Solomon seats Bathsheba beside him, provide the source.[1] The subject
is treated very similarly by the Master of Cappenberg in the Cappenberg
altarpiece and in a picture of the series in the Landesmuseum, Münster.[2]

For some comment on the series of which No. 263 is part, and its
provenance, see under No. 2154 below.

REPRODUCTION: *Illustrations, Continental Schools*, 1937, p. 399.

2154   CHRIST BEFORE PILATE

Pilate washing his hands; behind him his wife.

Oak, painted area, $39 \times 27\frac{1}{4}$ (0·991 × 0·692), including narrow borders
of brown and red paint at the top.

In good condition, despite some obvious paint losses in the lower part
of the picture, *e.g.* in the dog.

The treatment of the scene follows *Matthew*, xxvii, 19 and 24, though
Pilate's wife is not present there. Some further mention of her is in the

apocryphal *Acts of Pilate*, though not substantially different from the gospel account; she is traditionally called Claudia Procula.

The composition of No. 2154 may be compared with two treatments of the same scene by Derick Baegert: that at Nuremberg (itself derived in part from an engraving by Israhel van Meckenem[3]) and a version at Brussels[4] where Pilate and the boy pouring water for him are somewhat similar in pose to the same figures in No. 2154. The dog and the hands of Christ in No. 2154 are taken from an engraving of the subject by Schongauer.[5]

Nos. 263 and 2154 appear in the 1929 Gallery catalogue simply as of the Westphalian School; and it was apparently Friedländer who first attributed them to the Cappenberg Master.[6] The two pictures seem to belong to a group of eight panels, all of approximately the same size, forming a series of scenes from Christ's passion and after. All except one of this series passed into the Krüger collection, as the work of a later (sixteenth-century) Westphalian master, and with a provenance recorded from the Klosterkirche either at Liesborn or Marienfeld. The Krüger collection also contained a *Last Judgment* twice the height and twice the breadth of the single panels of the series, and with the same attribution and provenance. All these pictures were bought for the National Gallery, but only Nos. 263 and 2154 were retained.[7] The eight single panels, the whereabouts of which are fairly well established, are as follows: *Scourging at the Pillar*[8]; *Crowning with Thorns*[9]; No. 2154; *Christ carrying his Cross*[10]; *Resurrection*[11]; *Ascension*[12]; *Pentecost*[13]; No. 263.

On the basis of these facts, E. Mackowsky reconstructed an altarpiece of which the *Last Judgment* formed the central panel, with the series of eight smaller panels making up the wings[14]; she suggested that it might have been on one of the twenty-seven altars at Marienfeld.

It is, however, with Liesborn that the eight panels have recently been connected by A. Stange, who proposes that the panels constituted outside wings for the Liesborn high altarpiece and are in fact the two wings for it for which a payment is recorded to Jan Baegert.[15] The documents show that the panels from Liesborn (from the high altarpiece?) were sent to Wesel in 1517, but no reason is given nor is any painter named. Rensing supposed that the pictures went for restoration, since there are earlier accounts 'pro tabulis renovandis', in which painters are paid.[16] But since some panels (presumably the same ones) were later returned from Wesel, and since Jan Baegert, who worked at Wesel, was in 1520 paid for providing two wings for the Liesborn high altarpiece, it seems probable that what was sent to Wesel were the wings of the Liesborn altarpiece and that Jan Baegert painted the outside of them. Stange's proposal is that these outside panels for Liesborn are in fact the Cappenberg series, and this he supports by the striking fact that the eight Cappenberg panels can be divided into two wings of approximately the same area as (*i.e.* they could lie back to back with) the Liesborn wings.[17]

Against this identification, however, some objections can be made. The precise provenance from which the Cappenberg panels passed into the Krüger collection is not recorded, though it is true that Liesborn is mentioned as an alternative. It seems curious that Krüger should know the exact provenance (including 'from the high altarpiece') of the relevant Master of Liesborn fragments—but nothing of the Cappenberg Master panels which had the very same provenance.

More importantly, the inevitable arrangement (i.e. the narrative sequence) of the scenes of the Cappenberg wings results in an unusual final scene to the series: the *Coronation of the Virgin*. It is usual for Passion series of this type to end with a *Last Judgment*; and it would be a curiosity that this series ended with a *Coronation*.[18] One good reason why it should end thus would be, as Mackowsky supposed, that the *Last Judgment* was already shown in the central panel.

There is yet a further reason for doubting if the Cappenberg series was ever on the Liesborn high altar. Although the point cannot be established beyond doubt, there are grounds for supposing that the inner right-hand wing of that altarpiece showed the *Resurrection, Ascension, Pentecost* and *Last Judgment*.[19] In those circumstances it would hardly be credible that three of the same scenes were later repeated on the outside of the same wing. Indeed, if the Liesborn inner wing is correctly reconstructed above, it may be said to be virtually impossible that the Cappenberg series was ever on the outside. In which case, if these eight panels come from one altar (as their size and closely similar treatment each to the other suggest) then that altar is not the Liesborn high altar.

It is true that none of this explains away the fact that the Cappenberg and Liesborn panels coincide almost exactly in size. That, however, might be chance, for it must be remembered that Stange's identification ignores the hardly less striking fact that Krüger possessed a *Last Judgment* panel which would by its size serve very well as centrepiece to the Cappenberg pictures; and it shared with them attribution and provenance as well. Whichever solution is adopted, therefore, some element of chance in connection with the measurements has to be admitted.[20] From what has been said here it can be seen that it is not by any means established that Nos. 263 and 2154 were ever part of the Liesborn high altarpiece; and that Mackowsky's hypothesis is by no means invalidated. A date *ca.* 1520, or later, seems likely for the execution of the pictures.

PROVENANCE: From the Abbey church at Liesborn or Marienfeld.[21] In the Krüger Collection, Aachen, by 1833[22]; later in the same collection at Minden; purchased with the majority of the Krüger collection, 1854.

REPRODUCTION: (No. 2154). *Illustrations, Continental Schools*, 1937, p. 400.

REFERENCES : (1) See for instance J. J. M. Timmers, *Symboliek en Iconographie* . . . 1947, p. 444; for further discussion and other texts, see also A. Jameson, *Legends of the Madonna*, 1903 ed. pp. 94 ff., and K. Künstle, *Ikonographie der christlichen Kunst*, I, 1928, pp. 570 ff. (2) For the Münster picture see the Derick Baegert exhibition, Münster, Sept. 1937, no. 72; a photograph of the picture in the Gallery archives, kindly sent by Dr. Paul Pieper. (3) The Nuremberg picture in the Baegert catalogue, Münster, Sept. 1937, no. 37 and reproduced pl. XXVIII. The fashionable costume of Pilate's wife there may be contrasted with her equally fashionable but later costume in No. 2154; this suggests there is some gap of time between the two pictures. (4) Münster, Sept. 1937, no. 6 and pl. XVII. (5) Reproduced by J. Baum, *Martin Schongauer*, 1948, pl. 34; there is some resemblance also in the pose of Pilate and his servant. (6) Kaesbach, *op. cit.*, p. 39. (7) For the sale at Christie of the remainder, 14 February 1857, see Appendix II to this catalogue; the *Last Judgment* is not recorded since then. In addition, a tenth picture ex-Krüger and with the same provenance and attribution was bought by the National Gallery and included in the 1857 sale: *Christ before Caiaphas*, probably the picture called *Christ before Annas* in the J. G. Johnson collection, Philadelphia, *Johnson Catalogue*, III, 1914, No. 753; its present size (48 × 55) accords very nearly with that of the Krüger picture. It is thus twice as broad as the single Passion panels but seemed to bear no obvious relationship to them in height until it was cleaned. The picture before cleaning is reproduced by C. L. Kuhn, *A Catalogue of German Paintings . . . in American Collections*, 1936, pl. XVI. Cleaning of this picture has shown that it had been cut down, and overpainted to conceal the fact. It was originally somewhat higher and included two Passion scenes in the Garden of Gethsemane, and a central related scene, as well as the main subject; see the Johnson catalogue, 1941, p. 44 (under No. 753, Master of Kappenberg). A photograph since cleaning in the Gallery archives. (8) Landesmuseum, Münster; *Verzeichnis der Gemäldesammlung*, n.d. but post 1912, no. 66. (9) In a Christie sale, London, 15 December 1933 (lot 125), with *Christ carrying his Cross*, with forged Dürer monograms; attention was drawn to the true nature of these pictures by Martin Davies in *The Burlington Magazine*, LXV, 1934, p. 189. Further information and comment on them in G. van Oyen's catalogue, nos. 70–1. (10) See note 9 above. (11) Often published as lost: see for instance A. Stange in *Westfalen*, 1952, p. 199 (reconstruction of these panels as wings). But, as pointed out by G. van Oyen under her catalogue no. 68, acquired by the Landesmuseum, Münster, in 1942. (12) Landesmuseum, Münster: *Verzeichnis . . .* no. 67. (13) Not in the Krüger Collection but apparently passed into the collection at Schloss Herdringen about 1820–32. (14) E. Mackowsky in *The Burlington Magazine*, LXV, 1934, pp. 126 ff.; further Davies, *loc. cit.*, and Mackowsky, *ib.*, LXVI, 1935, p. 46, explicitly rejecting the Johnson picture which Davies had tentatively associated with the altarpiece. Mackowsky gives no substantial reason for her rejection and the note 7 here shows that Davies is likely to have been right in connecting this picture with the altarpiece under discussion. (15) A. Stange in *Westfalen*, 1952, pp. 198 ff. Stange's actual reconstruction as set out there (p. 199) is open to objection in the sequence of the left-hand wing and also contains an unfortunate misprint of 'Kreuzigung' for 'Kreuztragung'. (16) T. Rensing in *Westfalen*, 1937, p. 247. Stange, *loc. cit.*, makes a good point that the sum paid to Baegert (75 gulden) seems too high for mere restoration. (17) The sizes accord very closely indeed; compare Nos. 256–7 by the Master of Liesborn in this catalogue. These two pictures are essential to the case, since they are the only intact pictures of the Liesborn high altarpiece to survive. No. 256 alone survives on its original panel. (18) It should perhaps be added that a *Pentecost* scene is quite usual. What might seem an explanation of the *Coronation* at Liesborn is the fact that the high altar was dedicated to the Virgin, as well as to a group of saints. However, Marienfeld was a Cistercian foundation and hence had a devotion to the Virgin (who figured in a sculptured centre-piece on the high altar there). (19) It is usually agreed that the Lünen altarpiece, from the circle of the Liesborn Master, reproduces the same eight scenes which occurred at Liesborn, but of which only four can be certainly reconstructed from surviving fragments; these four do show that the Lünen versions are closely related in style and often in composition. For the Lünen altar see the exhibition, *Westfälische Maler der Spätgotik 1440–1490*, Münster, 1952, nos. 135–46 and pl. 42–3. The inner right-hand wing of the Lünen altar shows the four subjects mentioned in the text above. A point in support of at least one of these subjects appearing also in the relevant Liesborn wing is that the sole putative fragment from it (Head of an Apostle(?); Münster exhibition, 1952, no. 124) is so exactly similar in every way to the head of an Apostle in the Lünen *Ascension* as to suggest that there was an *Ascension* in the Liesborn series. (20) The Liesborn theory of Stange is accepted by G. van Oyen, *op. cit.*, pp. 67 ff., rejecting Mackowsky's identification partly on the grounds that the *Last Judgment* panel is slightly too small and that it is unlikely to have been cut down by a few centimetres all round. However, framing could well account for the very slight discrepancy, if discrepancy there is; and Stange's own theory quite reasonably supposes slight trimming of some panels, so that this could also have been done to the *Last Judgment*. And the Johnson *Christ before Caiaphas* is positive evidence of cutting down since it has been trimmed at the sides as well as top. (21) Krüger Catalogue, 1848, Part I, no. 38 *et seq.* for the provenance; (Nos. 263 and 2154 are there nos. 39 and 46). (22) See J. D. Passavant in *Kunst-Blatt*, 1833, p. 52, mentioning, however, only No. 263 and six others, 'Vorstellungen aus der Leidensgeschichte'; perhaps Krüger had not at that date acquired the *Last Judgment*.

MASTER of LIESBORN
Active second half of the XV century

He is named from the dismembered high altarpiece of the Benedictine abbey at Liesborn in Westphalia, and Nos. 256–261 catalogued below are fragments of this.

The high altar, with four other altars, is recorded as dedicated by the Abbot Heinrich von Kleve in 1465.[1] He is also recorded as having commissioned pictures for these altars, but it is not clear whether it should be inferred that any or all of these pictures were *in situ* at the time of the dedication.[2] The Abbot was enthroned in 1464 and died in 1490; the pictures seem to have been completed in his lifetime. Nordhoff supposed 1465 was the *terminus ante quem* for the Liesborn high altar-piece. Wormstall[3] thought it was rather the *terminus post quem*, and the present writer thinks the sense of the chronicler's passage agrees slightly better with Wormstall's view which is not always accepted by scholars. The high altarpiece, at least, remained *in situ* at Liesborn until the suppression of the abbey in 1803.

The Master of Liesborn was apparently active in various parts of Westphalia; a number of altarpieces are claimed as by or close to him. Nothing is recorded of his name or the location of his studio. There is Netherlandish influence in his style but transmitted no doubt through the fifteenth-century Cologne School, the influence of which is very apparent. Pictures with a good claim to be by the Liesborn Master himself are few, except for the surviving portions of the Liesborn high altarpiece.[4] Since so little is established, pictures catalogued here as near but not by him have all been placed under the heading 'Circle of the Master'.

REFERENCES: (1) Recorded in *Bernardi Witti, Historia . . . Westphaliae*, 1778, Appendix III, p. 773. Wittius was a novice at Liesborn in 1490, writing its chronicle *ca.* 1515–20. For full discussion, cf. J. B. Nordhoff, *Die Chronisten des Klosters Liesborn*, 1866 (reprinted from *Zeitschrift für vaterländische Geschichte . . .*, 1865, pp. 177 ff.). Later chroniclers, discussed by Nordhoff, seem to rely entirely on Wittius for this period—to judge by such MSS. as the present writer has seen at Münster. (2) The passage linked with the Master of Liesborn's pictures in J. Passavant, *Kunstreise durch England und Belgien*, 1833, p. 401, where it is quoted. (3) Cf. A. Wormstall in *Zeitschrift für vaterländische Geschichte* . . . , 1897, pp. 85 ff. (4) Further for the Master and his activity, see P. Pieper in the exhibition catalogue, *Westfälische Maler der Spätgotik*, Münster, 1952, under nos. 119 ff.; see also Pieper's addenda in *Westfalen*, 1954, pp. 75 ff. Some discussion of the whole question in A. Stange, *Deutsche Malerei der Gotik*: VI, *Nordwestdeutschland in der Zeit von 1450 bis 1515*, 1954, pp. 26 ff.

256 THE ANNUNCIATION

The Virgin's book with rubric beginning in two places: *O*. On the angel's scroll: *ave | gracia | pleñ | dominus | tecū*. On the two pillars left and right prophets(?), their scrolls unlettered. Between the two windows under a canopy a statue of God the Father. In the window panes and on the cushions some coats-of-arms (discussed in the text below).

Oak, painted surface, $38\frac{7}{8} \times 27\frac{3}{4}$ (0·962 × 0·705), including an original border of red paint at the lower and right-hand edges.

In very good condition; new gold on the Virgin's halo.

The scene is from S. Luke i, 26.

No. 256 is one of four panels forming the inside left-hand wing of the Liesborn high altarpiece. This inside wing can definitely be reconstructed as consisting of: No. 256, the *Nativity with Angels*,[1] the *Adoration of the Kings* (fragment, No. 258), the *Presentation in the Temple* (No. 257); the panels were arranged in two pairs one above the other, in the order given here. On analogy with some other altarpieces the right-hand inside wing is usually reconstructed[2] (though it is not likely that more than one fragment of it has survived[3]): the *Resurrection*, the *Ascension*, *Descent of the Holy Ghost*, and *Last Judgment*. It is probable that the Virgin appeared in all these scenes except the *Resurrection* panel. The central panel of the altarpiece showed the Crucifixion (fragments from it being Nos. 259–61 below).

No. 256 is unusual but not unique in showing the composition with the angel approaching from the right instead of from the left. The setting is an unusually detailed interior for a German master of the period and shows strong Netherlandish influences. The nearest parallels in German art are versions of the scene in the Master of Liesborn's manner and conceivably from his studio. It is uncommon in German art for coats-of-arms to be inserted in windows and furnishings outside the Master of Liesborn's circle; they do, however, occur quite commonly in Netherlandish art and in at least two scenes of the *Annunciation*, a version by Rogier van der Weyden[4] and the central panel of the Mérode triptych, both at New York. The arms in the windows of No. 256 are not very satisfactorily identified[5] but may be commented upon as follows, from left to right: (1) *d'or, à cinq boules gueules en barre*: apparently borne by a number of Westphalian families and, among others, those of Keppel, Pape, and Schladen have been named. (2) *d'argent à huit boules gueules rangées en orle*: Stael von Holstein. (3) *d'or à l'aigle eployée de sable*:

probably borne by a number of Westphalian families including that of Langen. (4) *d'or à la fasce de gueules*: variously borne but probably here for the state of Münster. The left-hand cushion shows a yellow stag running amid grass and trees, and must be a device rather than a coat-of-arms.[6] It does not relate apparently to any known Westphalian family; probably it is a mere coincidence that some of the patterned tiles of the floor also show a stag. The shield on the central cushion, *d'or à trois roses de gueules*, is borne by the families Billerbeck, Blome, Osten and Osterhausen.

The various arms must refer, presumably, either to donors of the altarpiece or to benefactors of the abbey; the arms of Abbot Heinrich von Kleve do not, however, seem to be represented. From the fragments remaining of the high altarpiece it seems that arms were introduced only into No. 256, perhaps because no other scene offered comparable opportunity. As is only too clear from the preceding paragraph, the evidence provided by the coats-of-arms is slight and confusing; the present writer has not pursued in great detail the question of which families named above had close links with the abbey of Liesborn (even supposing the facts could now be established).

It is reasonable to accept No. 256 as from the same hand as the central panel of the high altarpiece. The picture's quality is high and its condition, through the panel not having been transferred, is markedly better than the majority of other parts of the altarpiece catalogued below. As has been stated in the Master's biography, there is good reason to presume that the altarpiece does not date from much before 1465—at the very earliest. The furniture shown in No. 256 would apparently suggest a considerably later period,[7] and there is a case to be made—on stylistic grounds—for setting the whole altarpiece *ca.* 1480, or even later. Some further discussion is included under No. 261 below.[8]

For Provenance, etc., see also under No. 261.

VERSION: A version of the composition in reverse is at Lünen.[9]

REPRODUCTION: *Illustrations, Continental Schools*, 1937, p. 215.

257 THE PRESENTATION IN THE TEMPLE

On pillars in the background, left to right: a prophet with a book (Malachi?), David, Moses.

Panel transferred to canvas, $38\frac{3}{4} \times 27\frac{5}{8}$ (0·985 × 0·702), including an original border of red paint round all the edges.

In quite good condition under discoloured varnish; a few damages and some repaint.

The subject is from S. Luke ii, 24–5. The scene blends the Purification of the Virgin with the presentation of the Child to Simeon. Thus Moses appears in reference to the Mosaic law of purification (which required the offering of turtle doves, or pigeons, held here by the woman farthest left); David represents Christ's royal lineage; the prophet

Malachi does appear—as a bust—in at least one other version of the scene and some texts from his book are linked with the subject.[10] It is very unusual for S. Joseph to be omitted, as here, from the scene; some other Westphalian pictures of the period do, however, omit him.[11]

The position of No. 257 in the Liesborn high altarpiece has been indicated above. The handling seems rather cruder than that of No. 256, but this may be due in part to condition. It is reasonable to accept it as from the same hand.

For Provenance, etc., see under No. 261 below.

VERSION: A rather similar but less elaborate composition is at Lünen.

REPRODUCTION: *Illustrations, Continental Schools*, 1937, p. 216.

258 THE ADORATION OF THE KINGS

A fragment. The Child supported in the Virgin's lap and embraced by two Kings; the Virgin's hand holding a gold vessel. The background is of the ruined stable; at the left a stream. Extreme right a fold of drapery belonging to a further figure.

Oak, painted surface, $9\frac{1}{8} \times 15\frac{1}{4}$ (0·232 × 0·387).

In good condition; a few minor retouchings.

No. 258 is one of three surviving fragments of the original panel of the scene, whose position in the Liesborn high altarpiece has been indicated above. The remaining two fragments, showing respectively the head of S. Joseph and that of the third King, are at Münster. It is possible to reconstruct the composition fairly completely: the two kings of No. 258 were kneeling, the third was shown standing at the left. The drapery at the right of No. 258 belongs to S. Joseph who was also standing. There was a landscape background to the scene.

Possibly the head of the Virgin was also cut out of the original panel to make a fragment; if so, it seems not to have survived. Conceivably it was too damaged to be thought worth preserving.

The composition, as originally shown, is not exactly duplicated in other pictures of the subject by the Master of Liesborn or his circle.[12]

For Provenance, etc., see under No. 261 below.

REPRODUCTION: *Illustrations, Continental Schools*, 1937, p. 214.

259 HEAD OF CHRIST CRUCIFIED

A fragment. On the cross: *I.N.R.I.* A stamped pattern in the gold along the top edge of the picture. In the lower left-hand corner part of an angel's wing.

Oak, painted up to the edges, $12\frac{7}{8} \times 11\frac{3}{4}$ (0·327 × 0·298).

In good condition; a repainted damage on Christ's right arm, and small retouchings along all the edges.

No. 259 is a fragment from the central panel of the Liesborn high altarpiece. For discussion of this, Provenance, etc. see under No. 261 below.

REPRODUCTION: *Illustrations, Continental Schools*, 1937, p. 217.

260 SS. JOHN THE EVANGELIST, SCHOLASTICA AND
     BENEDICT

A fragment. A stamped pattern in the gold at the right-hand edge.
The haloes were all once inscribed, but are now illegible. The crook of
S. Scholastica's crozier ornamented with a scene of Abraham about to
slay Isaac; two male figures in the shaft of the crozier below.

Canvas transferred from panel, 22 × 27⅞ (0·559 × 0·708).

In quite good condition under discoloured varnish; but it has suffered
from transference. There are many minor losses and some repaint.

S. Benedict (†543), founder of the Benedictine order, is shown in the
black Benedictine habit and as abbot. S. Scholastica, his sister, is shown
as abbess of the order.

The Sacrifice of Isaac is a common Old Testament parallel to the
Crucifixion; No. 260 is a fragment from the central panel of the Liesborn
high altarpiece which showed the Crucifixion. Further discussion,
Provenance, etc. is under No. 261.

REPRODUCTION: *Illustrations, Continental Schools*, 1937, p. 215.

261 SS. COSMAS AND DAMIAN AND THE VIRGIN

A fragment. Stamped pattern in the gold at the left-hand edge. On
the haloes much damaged traces of the original names: S. Cosmas'
inscribed ...*M*..; S. Damian's ..*MIA*.; the Virgin's *MA*....*S*.
Cosmas holds a blue and white earthenware pot.[13]

Canvas transferred from panel, 21⅝ × 28⅜ (0·55 × 0·721).

In fair condition under discoloured varnish. The picture has suffered,
probably when being transferred, and there is quite extensive retouching. A minor *pentimento* in S. Damian's hand.

SS. Cosmas and Damian, twins, medical practitioners and martyrs,
were beheaded in 303. No. 261 is a fragment from the central panel of
the Liesborn high altarpiece, the Crucifixion, and their presence is
explained by the fact that the abbey was under their protection.

The central panel showed Christ crucified with the Virgin and saints
at either side, and angels above, against a gold background; it is not
clear whether any landscape was included. Apart from the portions
catalogued here, four further fragments (of angels) have survived and
are now in the Landesmuseum, Münster.[14] This is almost certainly the
correct complement of figures in the original panel, but Stange has
supposed there was a fifth angel now lost.[15] Reconstruction of the panel,
outlined in the subsequent paragraph, makes this unlikely.

The central panel has been reconstructed more than once by various
scholars[16] and doubt may possibly remain on the exact placing of some
of the angels. The stamped pattern which occurs on Nos. 259–61
establishes that these were placed at the extreme outside edges of the

panel: No. 259 centrally at the top, No. 260 at the right, No. 261 at the left. Two angels holding chalices and obviously intended as complementary were no doubt situated at either arm of the Cross. A third angel, also holding a chalice, seems to belong at the left of Christ (*i.e.* near the wound in his side) for the colour and pattern of its wings match the portion of wing on No. 259.[17] The fourth angel, the smallest fragment, is likely to have been situated near the fourth wound, *i.e.* at Christ's feet.[18] This arrangement, though possibly tentative to some extent, precludes the need for a fifth angel. A diagram of the proposed reconstruction, with some further comment, is in Appendix I.

Despite some diminution of quality owing to damage, the fragments catalogued here are clearly by the same hand as the better preserved Münster fragments of the central panel. There seems no variation in quality between this panel and the inside wings; it is therefore reasonable to suppose the whole altarpiece as originally placed *in situ* was by the Master of Liesborn (with or without studio assistance). Later additions to the wings of the altarpiece by Jan Baegert have been discussed in this catalogue already, under the Master of Cappenberg.

The possible date of the altarpiece has already been briefly discussed in the text of No. 256 above. Indications of date are few and uncertain. The altarpiece could hardly date from much before the reconsecration of the high altar in 1465 at which time it was dedicated (again?) to the Virgin, SS. Cosmas and Damian and S. Simeon the Prophet. Wittius says that Abbot Heinrich von Kleve commissioned the altarpieces, and he became abbot only in 1464. In fact, the implication of Wittius' chronicle is rather that the altarpieces followed the re-consecration; that sequence would also be more satisfactory for dating at least the high altarpiece, for it is under the influence of the Cologne School of the late fifteenth century (especially, it would seem, the later work of the Master of the Life of the Virgin [*q.v.*]). As explained in the biography of the Master of Liesborn above, the high altarpiece was apparently *in situ* by 1490. The present writer thinks, in sum, that the high altarpiece is unlikely to be from much before *ca.* 1475 and might even be from a few years later.

PROVENANCE: The altarpiece was painted for the Abbey Church at Liesborn and was still *in situ* on the high altar at the time of the abbey's suppression in 1803.[19] Cut up, partly destroyed, and dispersed in various collections, apparently in 1807. All the above pictures in the Krüger collection at Aachen by 1833 [20]; later at Minden.[21] Purchased with the majority of the collection, 1854.

REPRODUCTION: (No. 261) *Illustrations, Continental Schools*, 1937, p. 216.

REFERENCES: *General:* P. Pieper's catalogue of the exhibition at Münster, *Westfälische Maler der Spätgotik, 1440–1490*, 1952, nos. 119–24. Also Pieper's addenda in *Westfalen*, 1954, pp. 75 ff.

In text: (1) Two fragments from it survive at Münster, reproduced by Pieper, *op. cit.*, 1952, pl. 37. For opportunities to examine all the relevant fragments of the Liesborn high altarpiece at Münster, the present writer is indebted to Dr. Pieper and to Dr. H. Eickel. (2) Chiefly on analogy with the altarpiece at Lünen, from the circle of the Liesborn Master; cf. Pieper, *op. cit.*, 1952, nos. 135–46 (and plates 42–3). Compare also what is said on the question in this catalogue under Nos. 263 and 2154, Master of Cappenberg. **(3)** A head of a bearded man, arguably from this wing, catalogued by Pieper, *op. cit.*, 1952, no. 124 and reproduced pl. 54, then on the art market, Berlin. The head shows quite strong similarity in pose and appearance with that of one of the Apostles extreme left of the Lünen *Ascension*; compare further the note 19 to the Cappenberg Master entries in this catalogue. **(4)** H. B. Wehle and Margaretta Salinger, *The Metropolitan Museum of Art: A Catalogue of Early Flemish, Dutch and German Paintings*, 1947, pp. 38 ff. **(5)** A letter of 1933 from A. van de Put (in the Gallery archives) gives some notes on the coats-of-arms and is supplemented by Pieper's comments in the 1952 Münster exhibition catalogue. **(6)** The stag is not swimming, as Pieper, *loc. cit.*, supposes. He notes, however, that the device is not apparently connected with any Westphalian family and this remains true. **(7)** A letter of 1933 from Ralph Edwards (in the Gallery archives) comments on the furniture and setting of the picture. **(8)** It seems best to record here the comments of E. A. de la Torre in *Arte Español*, 1955, pp. 105 ff., who on analogy with the details of No. 256 (and some of the other Liesborn pictures) finds an affinity between them and a picture in the Prado, conceivably by Melchior Aleman. These comments are not concerned with the status of the Liesborn pictures. **(9)** For which see under Note 1. **(10)** The iconography of the subject in general is dealt with by Dorothy C. Shorr in *The Art Bulletin*, 1946, pp. 17 ff.; for the presence of Malachi and texts derived from him, *loc. cit.*, p. 28. **(11)** The panel of the altarpiece at Lünen, for example, probably derived from No. 257. An earlier example is the panel of the scene by the Master of the Fröndenberg Altarpiece; see the reproduction in the exhibition catalogue *Conrad von Soest*, Cappenberg (Dortmund) 1950, fig. 68. **(12)** Stange, *Deutsche Malerei . . .* VI, 1954, p. 28 notes that the composition may be derived in reverse from the Cologne Master of the Vision of S. John's *Adoration of the Kings* (Swiss private collection, reproduced by Stange, *Deutsche Malerei . . .* V, 1952, pl. 15); the chief difference is the placing and pose of S. Joseph. **(13)** Not of a type ever in existence, but vaguely derived from Hispano-Moresque pottery. A note on the subject, kindly provided by Arthur Lane, is in the Gallery archives. **(14)** For reproduction of these, see the exhibition catalogue, *Westfälische Maler . . .* 1952, pl. 35. **(15)** *Deutsche Malerei . . .* VI, 1954, pl. 27. **(16)** First commented upon and linked up with the passage in Wittius, *op. cit.*, by Passavant, *Kunstreise durch England und Belgien*, 1833, pp. 399 ff., followed by W. Lübke, *Die mittelalterliche Kunst in Westfalen*, 1853, pp. 346 ff., reconstructing the central panel with four angels. **(17)** The portion of wing on No. 259 would not accord with the other possible candidate, the fourth angel, whose wings are of different pattern and colour. Pieper in part proposed the same reconstruction on this point in his catalogue of 1952, *op. cit.* His alteration of it in *Westfalen*, 1954, p. 92 (under no. 119) is wrong. **(18)** For a similar placing compare for example Gert van Lon's *Crucifixion*, with four angels (at Münster): Stange, *op. cit.*, VI, 1954, pl. 76. **(19)** In general for the suppression, but unfortunately without any references to the pictures, see J. Linneborn in *Studien und Mittheilungen aus dem Benedictiner- und dem Cistercienser-Orden*, XXIII, 1902, pp. 309 ff., and pp. 588 ff. **(20)** Passavant, *loc. cit.* **(21)** Krüger catalogue, 1848, Part I, respectively nos. 14, 15, 16, 12, 10, 11.

Circle of the MASTER OF LIESBORN

254   SS. AMBROSE, EXUPERIUS AND JEROME

Their haloes inscribed: (.) *Ambrosius. eps.*; *.S'. exuperius. martir. & miles*; *.S'. Jheronim.'*

Panel transferred to canvas, $47\frac{1}{4} \times 26\frac{3}{4}$ ($1 \cdot 20 \times 0 \cdot 68$).

In good condition under discoloured varnish; a few small losses and retouchings.

For discussion, provenance, etc. see under No. 255 below.

REPRODUCTION: *Illustrations, Continental Schools*, 1937, p. 213.

255 SS. GREGORY, MAURICE AND AUGUSTINE

Their haloes inscribed: .*S.' gregorius.*; .*S.' m* (...). *martir.*; *S.'au* (...). The Annunciation is represented on S. Gregory's morse.

Panel transferred to canvas, $47\frac{1}{4} \times 26\frac{3}{4}$ ($1 \cdot 20 \times 0 \cdot 68$).

In good condition under discoloured varnish; damages on the haloes and in the architectural background. The condition is not quite so good as that of No. 254 above.

Previously the central figure of No. 255 has been called S. Hilary. The association of SS. Maurice and Exuperius is part of their legend: *primicerii* of the Theban legion, they were martyred probably *ca.* 303. Other saints, including S. Candidus, are sometimes associated with them. Since the central saint of No. 255 is shown as a soldier, it is of no importance that the word *miles* is omitted from his halo and the identification with S. Maurice need not be doubted.

The two pictures are clearly wings of an altarpiece, and a provenance from the abbey of Liesborn is recorded. In the 1929 National Gallery catalogue they were said to be from the high altarpiece there, which is not so. They have for long been associated with a picture of scenes from the *Legend of the True Cross* which might seem the central panel of the relevant altarpiece and which is rather similar in handling.[1] Yet as Pieper has pointed out, the architectural setting of Nos. 254-5 would be rather curious flanking that panel which has no similar architecture, and he has therefore supposed them to be the outside of the wings.[2] However, these outer panels are early recorded as showing *The Magdalen and S. John the Evangelist with Donor* and *S. James the Greater, with Donatrix* (the third figure missing).[3] It seems unreasonable to dismiss this evidence, which is Passavant's, and in fact it has remained until now undiscussed. Passavant believed the central panel to be lost, which is quite conceivable. *The Legend of the True Cross* panel, while it may be admitted to accord approximately in height with Nos. 254-5, is considerably too broad for them; nor has it in fact any provenance establishing it as from Liesborn. With the qualification mentioned above, Pieper accepts it as the central panel of the altarpiece of which Nos. 254-5 are the wings. Stange also connects the pictures and adds No. 262 below as the predella of this altarpiece.[4] The present writer considers there are strong objections to the identification, which cannot in any case be taken as established. And in general it may be noticed that chance plays its part in associating groups of Westphalian pictures which happen to agree with each other in dimensions much better than the group discussed here.

Nos. 254-5 were at one time supposed to be earlier than the Liesborn high altarpiece but from the same hand. In the 1929 catalogue they were catalogued as by the Master himself. However, the tendency of recent scholarship has been to recognize them as, while close to his hand, of lower quality. In the present state of knowledge it seems undesirable to attempt to catalogue them more precisely than as above. On the evidence of S. Maurice's armour, Sir James Mann thinks a date nearer 1460 than 1500 is likely.[5]

PROVENANCE: From the Abbey church at Liesborn.[6] In the Krüger collection, Minden, by 1840.[7] Purchased with the majority of the Krüger Collection, 1854.

REPRODUCTION: *Illustrations, Continental Schools*, 1937, p. 214.

REFERENCES: *General:* P. Pieper's catalogue of the exhibition at Münster, *Westfälische Maler der Spätgotik 1440–1490*, 1952, nos. 149–50. Also Pieper's addenda in *Westfalen*, 1954, pp. 75 ff.

In text: (1) In the von und zur Mühlen collection, Pieper, *op. cit.*, 1952, no. 148. The association of this picture with Nos. 254–5 was apparently first made by C. Becker in *Kunst-Blatt*, 1843, p. 370. F. Koch in *Westfalen*, 1913, p. 120 made the point that the pavement in No. 254 is repeated in the von und zur Mühlen picture's scene of the *Angel appearing to Constantine*. Sir James Mann kindly considered the armour shown in the zur Mühlen panel and in Nos. 254–5, at the present writer's request, and decided that from that point of view there was no objection to the association of the three pictures. (2) Pieper, *op. cit.*, 1952, discussion under Nos. 148–50. (3) Compare *Kunst-Blatt*, 1841, p. 417 and 1847, p. 23; Krüger Collection *Catalogue*, 1848, Part I, nos. 23–4 (as Later School of the Master of Liesborn). These pictures were sold at Christie, among the pictures not required for the National Gallery, 14 February 1857 (lots 13–14); see further Appendix II here. (4) *Deutsche Malerei . . . VI*, 1954, p. 30. Stange's point about No. 262 serving as a predella to this altarpiece is discussed further under that entry below. (5) Letter of 1958 in the Gallery archives. (6) It does not seem established that the pictures were there until the suppression of the abbey (1803). Stange, *loc. cit.*, has remarked that perhaps they had already been removed considerably before. (7) See *Kunst-Blatt*, 1841, p. 417; Krüger Catalogue, 1848, Part I, nos. 8–9 (as Master of Liesborn, First Period).

262   THE CRUCIFIXION WITH SAINTS

Left to right: SS. Scholastica, Mary Magdalene and Anne, the Virgin, Christ crucified, SS. John the Evangelist, Andrew, Benedict, Agnes. The Cross inscribed: *INRI.*

Oak, painted surface, $15\frac{1}{8} \times 46\frac{5}{8}$ (0·384 × 1·184).

In good condition; a few small retouchings and new gold on the haloes.

The saints in No. 262 are easily identifiable by the symbols which accompany them. For SS. Scholastica and Benedict, see under No. 260 above. S. Anne is shown with the Madonna and Child in her arms, the *Anna Selbdritt* depiction common in German art. S. Andrew, Apostle, is said to have been crucified at Patrae on the Black Sea; the tradition of his X-shaped Cross as here apparently dates from the fourteenth century. S. Agnes, Virgin, was martyred under Valerian *ca.* 258 and is usually accompanied as here by a lamb.

No. 262 is from the abbey at Liesborn, hence the appearance of SS. Benedict and Scholastica. To some extent the picture probably derives in composition from the central panel of the Liesborn high altarpiece.

Its shape suggests that it was intended as a predella, though predellas are not a common feature of Westphalian altarpieces. Stange[1] has proposed that No. 262 formed the predella of an altarpiece of the *Story of the True Cross*, of which Nos. 254–5 above were wings. The handling of No. 262 is rather different from them and the picture is of rather higher quality. More importantly, No. 262 is not nearly as wide as the central panel for which it is supposed to be the predella, a fact Pieper has already pointed out.[2] As has been remarked in the discussion under Nos. 254–5, the postulated reconstruction of this *True Cross* altarpiece is not very convincing and it may well be doubted in any case if No. 262 is related to it. Conceivably it served as predella for one of the other altarpieces—but not the high altarpiece—at Liesborn.

PROVENANCE: From the Abbey church at Liesborn.[3] In the Krüger collection, Minden, 1848.[4] Purchased with the majority of the Krüger collection, 1854.

REPRODUCTION: *Illustrations, Continental Schools*, 1937, p. 218.

REFERENCES: *General:* P. Pieper's catalogue of the Münster exhibition, *Westfälische Maler der Spätgotik 1440–1490*, 1952, no. 206. Also Pieper's addenda in *Westfalen*, 1954, pp. 75 ff.

In text: (1) *Deutsche Malerei* . . . VI, 1954, p. 30. (2) In *Westfalen, loc. cit.* (3) It does not seem established that the picture remained there until the suppression of the abbey (1803). (4) Krüger Catalogue, 1848, Part I, No. 25.

2151 THE VIRGIN AND CHILD WITH A DONOR

Two angels crown the Virgin with a wreath of roses. Kneeling at the right the donor, a monk, at whose left a scroll inscribed (some letters repainted wrongly): ·*miser'e mei clemētissīē* . . . *miā z tuā ɣ p it'cessīœ z dulcissīē gēit'cis tue lucē m̄ cōcede ppetuā*

Oak, painted surface, 46¾ × 20¼ (1·188 × 0·515).

In rather poor condition under discoloured varnish. There is probably extensive wearing and certainly considerable repainting, most apparent in the flesh; there are a number of damages. A heavy layer of brownish repaint covers the Virgin's dress which can be seen in places to have been originally patterned red and gold[1] (some of it is preserved under the repaint). A slight *pentimento* in the donor's head.

The donor in No. 2151 is presumably a Benedictine monk, to judge from his black habit; the collar he wears is obviously anachronistic and in fact the area of his head is a piece of wood 5⅞ × 4¾ (0·148 × 0·12) apparently inserted and painted in the nineteenth century. The significance of this is dealt with further below. The portion of the scroll where there is a gap is part of the inserted panel which contains one or two nonsense letters. The text of the scroll has very kindly been deciphered by Francis Wormald who has also suggested the emendations which are proposed below.[2] The expanded text reads: *miserere mei clementissime . . . misericordiam tuam et per intercessionem dulcissime genetricis tue lucem mihi concede perpetuam.* The sense clearly requires for the missing portion first some such word as *Domine*, probably in abbreviation the words: *Domine Jesu Christe*; and is likely to have continued: *secundum (magnam?).*

The iconography of No. 2151 is interesting, because the picture seems to be a rather early example of the Rosary Madonna type of image. Perhaps the earliest comparable picture is the central panel of Antonello da Messina's *S. Gregory polytych* (dated 1473).[3] What is apparently of some years later is the elaborate *Rosary altarpiece* by the Master of S. Severin in S. Andreas at Cologne[4]; the complete altarpiece of which No. 2151 is part may well have been analogous to the latter in appearance.

No. 2151 has already been published by the present writer as the central panel of the Herzebrock altar. This altarpiece was dismembered at the suppression of the Benedictine convent of Herzebrock, but in addition to No. 2151 some portions of it survive at Münster. There are two wings, each of four scenes from the life of the Virgin, and a small fragment of a monk's head which has in fact been cut from No. 2151 [5]; to conceal this the insertion mentioned above was made, but for some reason the monk's original cowl was replaced by the seventeenth-century style collar.[6] As the Münster fragment has always been recorded from Herzebrock, it is clear that No. 2151 is the central panel which had been mentioned by Lübke,[7] and since usually supposed lost or destroyed.

The London/Münster portions cannot, it seems, by themselves have formed the complete altarpiece, for the wings are considerably too wide for the central panel—though according in height. What the dimensions would suggest is that there were two flanking panels to No. 2151 (making a fixed centre of approximately 150 cm.) and that the Münster wings closed over this (their width when closed is approximately 154 cm.). Conceivably these two panels showed the patronesses of Herzebrock, SS. Christina and Petronella, possibly with figures of nuns at their feet.[8] Although this remains obviously hypothetical, a somewhat similar effect is given by the wings of an altarpiece by the Master of Liesborn, the *Resurrection* altar for the Franciscan convent of S. Clare, Cologne. And the format of the Herzebrock altar would also, on the hypothesis advanced above, show analogies with the *Rosary* altarpiece by the Master of S. Severin.

No. 2151 was in the Krüger collection simply as of the Westphalian School and has previously been so catalogued. Friedländer's opinion that it was related to the Master of Liesborn is recorded,[9] and is now confirmed. The Münster wings were given by F. Koch to the 'Master of 1489',[10] but it is very doubtful if this term represents a specific personality. H. Busch has related the pictures back to the Master of Liesborn.[11] Stange more plausibly suggests that they are the work of an assistant.[12] The present writer thinks No. 2151 may have had quite a good claim to be considered from the Master of Liesborn's studio, but its present condition is a grave handicap to attribution. It therefore seems best to catalogue it no more exactly than as above. The quality of it and the Münster wings (themselves inferior in handling to No. 2151) do not seem to the present writer high enough for them to be by the Liesborn Master himself.

The date of execution is likely to be late in the fifteenth century, as the apparent subject of the Rosary Madonna indicates; indeed, if No. 2151 is intended as an actual Rosary Madonna, it is unlikely to date from much before 1470 when Alain de la Roche popularised the symbolic link between the rosary and a crown of roses.[13] Busch dates the Herzebrock wings between the Liesborn high altar (of 1465?) and the '1489' *Noli Me Tangere* altar from Soest.[14] It is perhaps worth adding that *ca.* 1474 there was some rebuilding activity at the Herzebrock convent and conceivably the commission for the altarpiece originated at that period.[15]

PROVENANCE: From the Benedictine Convent at Herzebrock, near Rheda. In the Krüger collection, Minden, by 1848.[16] Bought with the majority of the collection, 1854.

REPRODUCTION: *Illustrations, Continental Schools,* 1937, p. 400.

REFERENCES: *General:* The present writer in *The Burlington Magazine,* C, 1958, pp. 304 ff.

In text: (1) It thus accords with the Virgin's dress in the scenes from her life which formed the wings of No. 2151 and which are mentioned in the text below. (2) The present writer is greatly indebted to Francis Wormald for his help and comments. The text of the scroll given above corrects that given by the present writer, *loc. cit.* which was supplied from a note in the Gallery archives where the text is connected with part of the office for the feast of S. Vincent Ferrer. There is, however, no similarity between the text of No. 2151 and any passage in the office for that day; the text seems to be merely a pious ejaculation. (3) Cf. K. Künstle, *Ikonographie der christlichen Kunst,* I, 1928, pp. 638 ff., for discussion of the subject in general and reproduction of the Antonello. (4) Künstle, *loc. cit.*; for discussion of the date of this altarpiece see A. Stange, *Deutsche Malerei . . . :* V, *Köln in der Zeit von 1450 bis 1515,* 1952, pp. 109–10. (5) For these pictures, see the catalogue, *Westfälische Maler der Spätgotik 1440–1490,* Münster, 1952, nos. 183–91; the two wings are reproduced in *Die Bau-und Kunstdenkmäler von Westfalen (Kreis Wiedenbruck)* 1901, pl. 13. (6) Presumably this indicates that the Münster fragment was not available for copying; yet the head in No. 2151 does seem to be derived from it. (7) Cf. W. Lübke, *Die mittelalterliche Kunst in Westfalen,* 1853, p. 352, remarking that the central panel belonged to Krüger. (8) Künstle, *loc. cit.,* remarks on the tendency of Rosary Madonna depictions to become types also of the Madonna *della Misericordia.* (9) Note in the Gallery archives. (10) Münster catalogue: *Verzeichnis . . .* n.d., pp. 15–16. (11) *Meister des Nordens,* 1943 ed., pp. 75–6. (12) *Deutsche Malerei . . .* VI: *Nordwestdeutschland in der Zeit von 1450 bis 1515,* 1954, p. 35. Among the pictures Stange associates with this hand, the Amelsbüren altarpiece wing, *S. John the Baptist and the Virgin,* shows quite close analogies with No. 2151. (13) See E. Mâle, *L'Art religieux de la fin du Moyen Age en France,* 1922 ed., p. 207. However, the most obvious lack in No. 2151 is in fact a rosary. The gesture of the Child's left hand might encourage the idea that he held a rosary, or at least some object, but technical photographs reveal nothing in his hand. (14) *Loc. cit.* (15) A further possible indication of date might be deduced from the donor in No. 2151. New regulations for the Herzebrock Convent were confirmed in 1477 by Sixtus IV and by these the nuns' confessor was to be either a secular priest or a Benedictine monk (*Die Bau- und Kunstdenkmäler . . . op. cit.,* p. 30). Such a monk might well be the donor of the altarpiece, but it is unfortunately not clear what were the previous regulations at Herzebrock and whether a Benedictine monk had usually been the nuns' confessor. The point is worth comment here chiefly because it might accord with the other vague indications of date for the altarpiece. (16) Krüger

Catalogue, 1848, Part I, no. 47, as by an unknown master of the Westphalian School, without provenance.

2152 S. DOROTHY

She wears a wreath of roses and holds a rose in her right hand; in her left hand a basket of roses. On her halo: *Scta. dorotea* (repainted).

Oak, $31\frac{5}{8} \times 19$ (0·804 × 0·483), painted up to the edges.

In poor condition; considerably damaged and extensively repainted. The gold of the halo is new and the bank of grass and flowers is repainted. The hills at the right and the sky are largely false.

S. Dorothy, Virgin Martyr, is said to have suffered under Diocletian. The roses are those sent from Paradise when a certain Theophilus mocked the saint on her way to martyrdom. In Germany S. Dorothy was included among the fourteen Helpers in Need and was popular in art.

The picture is a fragment from a larger picture. For further discussion, Provenance, etc. see under No. 2153 below.

REPRODUCTION: *Illustrations, Continental Schools*, 1937, p. 217.

2153 S. MARGARET

She wears a headdress of pearls. In her right hand a cross. In her left the chain of her dragon on whom she is sitting. On her halo: *Sancta. Margarit* (repainted).

Oak, $31\frac{3}{4} \times 18\frac{7}{8}$ (0·807 × 0·48), painted up to the edges.

In fair condition; there are some damages and considerable repaint but not greatly affecting the saint. The gold of the halo is new, and the background of sky and hills is largely false.

S. Margaret, Virgin Martyr, died at the beginning of the fourth century. She is commonly shown with a dragon whom she overcame by making the sign of the Cross, either over it or when inside it. In the latter case it burst and disgorged her. She is often shown holding a small cross as here.

Nos. 2152–3 are recorded as from a chapel at Lippstadt, with some further pictures.[1] Two of these were of SS. Barbara and Agnes, rather smaller panels than the two under discussion[2]; they seem now to be lost. A third picture, the *Ascension*, considerably larger than Nos. 2152–3, but with the same provenance, also exists[3]; it is probably unrelated to the altarpiece from which the other pictures come.

In conversation with the present writer, Dr. Paul Pieper suggested that Nos. 2152–3 might be fragments of a single large picture, and X-ray photographs confirm this supposition. The pictures have clearly been repainted to conceal the fact that they are fragments and the falseness of the background in both is quite obvious. X-ray photographs show some faint traces of drapery in the sky to the right of S. Dorothy's head; in the grass at her right (repainted) they show an object which is almost certainly a wheel. Behind S. Margaret's head are revealed a hand and folds of drapery, which belong to a seated figure; there are very faint traces of this apparent to the naked eye under the false sky, and it seems to have been red. To the left of this figure is the lower half of a lamb, standing on its hind legs and obviously reaching up to the outstretched hand just above. The area is damaged, but there can be no doubt that the animal is correctly identified as a lamb.[4] This figure must therefore be S. Agnes, and no doubt the upper half of her was the picture already referred to as now lost. The complete figure would be on a rather smaller scale than S. Margaret.

It would then be likely that there was a female saint near S. Dorothy, and the indications are that this would be S. Catherine. Possibly the other missing fragment called S. Barbara was really a S. Catherine wrongly identified. At any rate, it seems clear that the four fragments of female martyrs belonged in a single large panel. To judge from the setting of Nos. 2152–3, this was probably a *hortus conclusus* scene, with the Virgin and Child. The pose of S. Dorothy suggests she is in fact offering a flower, probably to the Child. In such depictions in German art it is quite common for S. Anne to appear with the Virgin and Child, and there is some slight reason for supposing she might have appeared in the panel under discussion.

The two lost(?) fragments and Nos. 2152–3 are recorded as from a chapel at Lippstadt. If this is to be interpreted literally as in Lippstadt itself, the choice of provenance is very restricted. The majority of churches and chapels there were suppressed and reformed in Lutheran times. As far as the present writer can trace, only one foundation was suppressed at Lippstadt in the early nineteenth century—and it is reasonable to suppose that it was recent suppression that put the pictures on the market whence they were purchased by Krüger (see under Provenance). This foundation was the Augustinian convent of S. Anna Rosengarten, suppressed shortly before 1822, it seems.[5] The chapel of this convent had, it is true, technically become a church long before; but perhaps it is possible that it was loosely described as a chapel since it served as one for the canonesses. The title of the convent, founded 1431–5, might seem to make such a subject as proposed above very appropriate. The size of the original panel must have been quite large, and it no doubt served as an altarpiece. The present writer has not managed to trace any other fragments which might belong to the original picture.

The present entry must be tentative, not only in reconstructing the panel from which Nos. 2152–3 probably come, but in commenting on what exactly lies beneath the surface of the two pictures. Cleaning of them would provide a good deal more certainty on this point; it is unfortunate that they are damaged, and their quality seems never to have been very high.

Stange has associated Nos. 2152–3 along with some other pictures, as close to the so-called Nikolaus Uelnmeigr.[6] The existence of this painter is a rather doubtful matter. The relevant altarpiece at Münster, supposedly signed by him, is judged by the present writer to be certainly by a different hand from Nos. 2152–3, whatever its own status.[7] All that can be said further is that the two pictures catalogued here do not appear to be by the hand of Nos. 254–5 above, and that even allowing for damage they seem some way from the handling of the Liesborn high altarpiece.

PROVENANCE : Recorded as from a chapel at Lippstadt. In the Krüger collection, Minden, by 1848.[8] Purchased with the majority of the collection, 1854.

REPRODUCTION : *Illustrations, Continental Schools*, 1937, p. 218.

REFERENCES : *General:* Pieper, *op. cit.*, 1952 and 1954.

In text: (1) Cf. the Krüger catalogue, 1848, I, nos. 18–22. (2) Included in the Christie sale of 1857, lots 11 and 12; for this sale see further Appendix II. (3) Included in the Christie sale, 1857 (lot 10), now in the parish church, Brant Broughton. It is Pieper, *op. cit.*, 1952, no. 204 and pl. 56. (4) The lamb accompanying S. Agnes in another Liesborn circle picture, No. 262 of this catalogue, is exactly similar in pose. (5) The date is from L. Schmitz-Kallenberg, *Monasticon Westfaliae*, 1909, p. 42; it is given as 1814 in *Die Bau- und Kunstdenkmäler . . . (Kreis Lippstadt)*, 1912, p. 102. For further details, cf. R. Chalybaeus, *Lippstadt*, 1876, pp. 96 ff. (6) See Stange, *Deutsche Malerei . . . VI*, 1954, pp. 38 ff. The painter has usually been discussed under the name N. Suelnmeigr: under which compare also the sceptical notice of K. Hölker in Thieme-Becker *Lexikon*, XXXII, 1938. (7) For this picture see Pieper, *op. cit.*, 1952, nos. 192–6 with full discussion; also Stange, *loc. cit.* It is catalogued by Pieper as 'Umkreis' of the Master of Liesborn but shown at Münster (at least in 1957) as by Uelnmeigr. (8) Krüger catalogue, 1848, Part I, nos. 19–20, with previous provenance.

MASTER of the LIFE OF THE VIRGIN
Active second half of the XV century

He is named from a series of eight panels of the *Life of the Virgin*, of which No. 706 below is one; the remainder are at Munich. He was apparently active at Cologne. No pictures are dated, but a *Crucifixion* (at Cues, on the Moselle), always accepted as his work, is probably of about 1465. A *Deposition*, central panel of the Tersteegen de Monte altarpiece (at Cologne), is probably of about 1480. These dates are not necessarily the limits of the Master's activity. All the pictures associated with him, including the *Life of the Virgin* series, show strong Netherlandish influence, especially that of Dieric Bouts and Rogier van der Weyden; it is possible that the Master was trained in the Netherlands.

The name *Master of the Lyversberg Passion* (from a Passion series at Cologne) was at one time applied to him, but is now usually reserved to indicate a supposedly different hand. There seem difficulties of chronology in accepting Förster's thesis[1] that all these pictures are in fact by one hand; but stylistically the Lyversberg Master is so close to the Master of the Life of the Virgin that there is much to be said for Förster's thesis.[2] In any event, the relationship between the two groups of pictures is very close indeed. An acceptable chronology for the Master of the Life of the Virgin group is yet to be proposed.

REFERENCES: (1) O. Förster in *Wallraf-Richartz Jahrbuch*, 1926–7, pp. 152 ff. For the literature on the whole subject, see H. Kisky in Thieme-Becker *Lexikon*, XXXVII. (2) It is rejected by A. Stange, *Deutsche Malerei . . .* V: *Köln in der Zeit von 1450 bis 1515*, 1952, pp. 37 ff.

706 THE PRESENTATION IN THE TEMPLE

Simeon receives the Infant from the Virgin; there are traces of her name on her halo. S. Joseph with one hand in his purse; behind him a woman holding a pair of doves. Right of the altar a woman holding a candle and apparently indicating the central incident to a richly dressed man. The retable is inscribed: *ANGLÆE;* three scenes are illustrated above (left to right): the *Offering of Cain and Abel* and *Murder of Abel* (in one); *Sacrifice of Isaac*; the *Drunkenness of Noah*. On the dorsal of Simeon's cope the vision of Augustus and the Tiburtine Sibyl; of the single figures along the edge of the cope Moses is identifiable.

Oak, painted surface, 33 × 42¾ (0·84 × 1·085).

In good condition. Very slight damages along a vertical crack running through the retable right of centre; some damages in the gold background. Cleaned in 1957.

The subject is from S. Luke ii, 24–5.

The Presentation in the Temple represents also the Purification of the Virgin and thus figures as an incident in her life.[1] The doves were part of the ritual purification prescribed by Mosaic law, as was also the payment of gold shekels. The figures at the right of the altar seem to have some special significance; the costume of the woman is in fact close to that of the Tiburtine Sibyl on Simeon's cope, and the man's costume is quite unlike that of any other figure in No. 706 or in the series of which this picture is part. However, the present writer has found no source for any departure from the usual iconography of the scene.

The inscribed word on the retable is presumably for *Angularis*, a reference to the cornerstone of the Temple, *Lapis Angularis*, which the builders rejected.[2] In the New Testament it is typologically used for Christ and the passage of S. Paul (*Ephesians* ii, 19–20) in which Christ is the 'chief cornerstone' is illustrated by, for example, Jean Pucelle in the 'Belleville Breviary'.[3] The three scenes on the retable are Old Testament parallels to Christ's Passion. Abel and Isaac are obvious prototypes[4]; the *Drunkenness of Noah*, or rather his nudity at the time, is paralleled by S. Augustine with Christ stripped at the Passion[5] and it became an accepted parallel in painting (*e.g.* Michelangelo's scene on the Sistine Chapel ceiling).

The subject of Augustus and the Sibyl is not common in Northern painting before the fifteenth century.[6] The scene takes place in No. 706 in a room (as it does in Rogier van der Weyden's altarpiece at Berlin)[7] but traditionally the Sibyl revealed a vision of the Virgin and Child to the Emperor on the Capitol, while a voice spoke: *Haec est ara cœli*.

No 706 is one of a series of eight panels of the life of the Virgin, from which the Master takes his name; as already mentioned, the remaining panels are at Munich. The donor of the series was Dr. Johann von Schwartz-Hirtz, Counsellor at Cologne from 1439 to 1460[8]; his portrait and his arms are introduced into the scene of *The Visitation*. The pictures come from S. Ursula's, Cologne, and originally formed an altarpiece, arranged in two rows, from left to right (top): (1) *Meeting at the Golden Gate*, (2) *Birth of the Virgin*, (3) *Presentation of the Virgin*, (4) *Marriage of the Virgin*; (below): (5) *Annunciation*, (6) *Visitation*, (7) No. 706, (8) *Assumption*. Of these, 1 and 5 formed the left wing and have on the back remains of a *Crucifixion*; 4 and 8 formed the right wing and have on the back a *Coronation of the Virgin*. The remaining four panels have nothing on the back and presumably formed the fixed centre-piece of the altar.[9]

There is little or no evidence for arriving at a date of execution. Stange tentatively proposed the early part of the decade of 1460 as the likely period.[10] H. Kisky suggests a later date, early in the 1470's.[11] The present writer thinks Stange's dating the more convincing.

PROVENANCE: From S. Ursula's, Cologne, and the series is probably that referred to in the church soon after 1500.[12] The series acquired by the brothers Sulpiz and Melchior Boisserée from the church, 12 March 1812.[13]. No. 706 exchanged by them with Count Joseph von Rechberg in the autumn of 1815 [14] and later that year passed into the collection of Prince Ludwig Kraft Ernst von Oettingen-Wallerstein[15]; at Schloss Wallerstein.[16] Exhibited for sale at Kensington Palace, 1848 (No. 64),[17] bought with the rest of the collection by the Prince Consort; at Kensington Palace, 1854.[18] Exhibited at Manchester, 1857 (Provisional Catalogue, no. 437; Definitive Catalogue, no. 379), lent by Prince Albert. Presented by Queen Victoria, at the Prince Consort's wish, 1863.

REPRODUCTION: *Illustrations, Continental Schools*, 1937, p. 219.

REFERENCES: (1) For some discussion of the iconography of the scene, cf. D. Shorr in *Art Bulletin*, 1946, pp. 17 ff. (2) A note in the Gallery archives that this was suggested 'by the Dominicans'. (3) See the description of this scene given in the first volume of the psalter, quoted in E. G. Holt, *A Documentary History of Art*, I, 1957, p. 132. (4) It is common for the *Sacrifice of Isaac* to appear on the retable in scenes of the *Presentation*: examples from the following of the Master of the Life of the Virgin include that by the Master of the Aachen Cupboard Doors (Stange, *Deutsche Malerei* . . . V: *Köln* . . . 1952, pl. 112) and that by the Master of the Lyversberg Passion (Stange, *op. cit.*, pl. 84). (5) Cf. E. Mâle, *L'Art religieux du XIIIe siècle en France*, 1923, p. 138; on Abel and Isaac as prototypes, Mâle *passim*. (6) Popularized in the North by its appearance in the *Speculum humanae Salvationis*; cf. E. Mâle, *L'Art Religieux de la fin du Moyen Age*, 1922, p. 236. (7) Perhaps it is not a coincidence that the poses of Augustus and the Sibyl in No. 706 remind one of the poses of the same two figures in Rogier's picture. (8) For some discussion about his identity, see E. Firmenich-Richartz, *Die Brüder Boisserée*, vol. I, 1916, p. 461. (9) For some comment on the formation of the altarpiece, see C. Aldenhoven, *Geschichte der Kölner Malerschule*, 1902, p. 411, note 347A, also the reconstruction in Stange, *op. cit.*, p. 26. (10) *Op. cit.*, p. 29. (11) Thieme-Becker *Lexikon*, XXXVII, *ad vocem*. (12) By Ortuinus Gratius (Codex 162 of the Cathedral archives, Cologne): the text published by Aldenhoven, *op. cit.*, p. 411, note 350. The reference is not quite accurate but does seem to refer to the Master's series of which No. 706 is part. (13) Cf. E. Firmenich-Richartz, *op. cit.*, p. 460. (14) In exchange for a supposed Carel van Mander, cf. Firmenich-Richartz, *loc. cit.* (15) For the date, see *Kunst-Blatt*, 1824, p. 353; what is probably No. 706 is referred to, *loc. cit.*, p. 318. Some further literature on the collection in general, referred to under

Lochner, No. 705, of this catalogue. (16) Lithographed catalogue of 1826(?) no. 73, Israel von Mecheln, as ex-Boisserée; 1827 MS. Catalogue, same number and attribution (copies in the Gallery archives; originals in the Alte Pinakothek, Munich). (17) Under previous attribution. (18) Waagen's catalogue, 1854, no. 23, as Master of the Lyversberg Passion and so exhibited at Manchester, 1857, (see Provenance further).

Studio of the MASTER OF THE LIFE OF THE VIRGIN

250 SS. JEROME, BERNARD(?), GILES AND BENEDICT(?)

SS. Jerome and Giles are accompanied respectively by a lion and a hind.

Panel transferred to canvas, original painted area, $48\frac{3}{4} \times 32\frac{1}{2}$ ($1 \cdot 238 \times 0 \cdot 825$).

In fair condition. Rather damaged from transference.

S. Giles (Aegydius) is often shown, as here, as a Benedictine abbot; the hind accompanied him into the desert. SS. Bernard and Benedict were proposed by E. Beck for the other two saints.[1] The provenance of No. 250 from the Benedictine abbey of Werden (see further below under No. 253) makes it more likely that S. Benedict appears here than the previously proposed S. Romuald. Here his habit is white and he does sometimes appear in white, e.g. in Francia's altarpiece No. 179 of this Gallery.[2]

No. 250 is the outside right-hand wing of the Werden altarpiece, of which No. 253 below is the inside right wing and Nos. 251–2 formed the left-hand wing. The attribution and provenance are discussed under No. 253.

REPRODUCTION : *Illustrations, Continental Schools*, 1937, p. 223.

251 SS. AUGUSTINE, LUDGER(?), HUBERT AND GEREON(?)

S. Augustine holds a heart pierced by an arrow. On the morse of S. Ludger's(?) cope the Virgin and Child enthroned and adored by two angels. S. Hubert holds a book with a stag seated on it.

Oak, painted surface, $48\frac{3}{4} \times 32\frac{3}{4}$ ($1 \cdot 238 \times 0 \cdot 83$).

In quite good condition; the gold haloes are damaged.

S. Ludger was the founder of the abbey at Werden *ca.* 800 and is likely to be the bishop saint of No. 251. Previously the warrior saint has been identified as S. Maurice; but the figure is very close indeed to other depictions of S. Gereon who, according to some accounts, was also a member of the Theban legion.

No. 251 is the outside left-hand wing of the Werden altarpiece which is discussed further under No. 253 below.

REPRODUCTION : *Illustrations, Continental Schools*, 1937, p. 224.

252 THE CONVERSION OF S. HUBERT

S. Hubert kneeling centre before a stag bearing a Crucifix between its antlers, the Cross inscribed *INRI*. In the distance scenes of hunting and hawking.

Oak, painted surface, $48\frac{3}{4} \times 32\frac{3}{4}$ (1.238×0.83).

In good condition. The gold of the halo and background is new.

S. Hubert (*ca.* 656–727) was first bishop of Liège. The story of the miraculous stag which appeared to him while out hunting has been introduced into his legend by confusion with the story of S. Eustace. The stag is said to have appeared to S. Hubert in the forest of the Ardennes.

No. 252 is the inside left-hand wing of the Werden altar. Although this series is discussed below, it should be emphasized here that the quality of No. 252 is very high, partly because it has not suffered transference and probably because the inner wings of the Werden altar were always of higher quality than the outer. Its importance for establishing the attribution of these four pictures is therefore considerable. Further, it contains some costume indications, chiefly in S. Hubert's dress, which suggest that it cannot have been painted before about 1480 and is likely to be late in that decade.[3]

REPRODUCTION: *Illustrations, Continental Schools*, 1937, p. 223.

253 THE MASS OF S. HUBERT

An angel brings S. Hubert a stole while he is saying mass. On the retable God the Father, flanked by SS. Peter and Paul. Right foreground a dog.

Panel transferred to canvas, original painted area, $48\frac{1}{2} \times 32\frac{3}{4}$ (1.232×0.83).

In quite good condition under discoloured varnish. There are damages on the retable; the gold of it and the background is new.

The subject of the scene does not seem usually to appear in lives of S. Hubert. According to the Bollandists an angel appeared with a stole for S. Hubert when he was being consecrated bishop by the Pope[4]; in No. 253 S. Hubert is already a bishop, the deacon behind him holding his mitre and crozier. In some depictions the angel brings S. Hubert the stole at the moment of his conversion. Perhaps the iconography as in No. 253 grew out of treatments of the somewhat similar *Mass of S. Giles*. The dog in the church in No. 253 is not irrelevant since S. Hubert was protector against, among other things, hydrophobia.

No. 253 is the inner right wing of the Werden altar. It does not seem possible to establish for what altar at Werden these two wings were intended, but it was not the high altar[5]; nor is it known if there was a central panel, now lost. They have hitherto been catalogued as by the 'Master of Werden'[6] but the name rightly has not entered scholarship. There can be no doubt that the style of the pictures is close to that of the Master of the Life of the Virgin; attributions have varied only in assessing their degree of closeness to the Master. By Crowe and Cavalcaselle they were ascribed to the supposed pupil, the Master of the Lyversberg Passion.[7] Brockmann ascribed them to the pupil who painted a *Mass of S. Gregory* in S. Cunibert's, Cologne.[8] This pupil has been identified as the Master of the S. George Legend and Nos. 250-3 are ascribed by Stange to this painter.[9] Friedländer apparently placed Nos. 250-3 between the Master of the Life and the Master of the Lyversberg Passion.[10]

However, Scheibler, Firmenich-Richartz, and Aldenhoven accepted the pictures as by the Master of the Life, with workshop assistance for the outer wings[11]; Reiners rejected this, without offering a very clear alternative.[12] The present writer believes that the view of Scheibler, and those agreeing with him, is the correct explanation. The ascription to the Lyversberg Master is a doubtful matter; Friedländer's ascription creates yet another personality (the Master of Werden in fact); the recent attribution by Stange is not borne out by examination of, above all, the S. George panels after which the S. George Master is named. These are considerably coarser in execution and the hand is altogether feebler than that on Nos. 252-3, *i.e.* the inner Werden wings.

The analogies between No. 252 and pictures accepted as late work by the Life of the Virgin Master are very close indeed. The central panel of the Tersteegen altarpiece, the *Crucifixion*, may be cited as one example. Wings (at Cologne) from another altarpiece by the Master and his studio, showing the same discrepancy between inside and outside as the Werden series, are usually dated about 1490.[13] The inside wings there show very strong similarities of handling with No. 252.

Costume indications in No. 252, as already mentioned, suggest that that picture can hardly be before 1480 and is likely to date rather from 1485-90. Stylistic indications accord with this quite well, and perhaps the abbey's history also accords: for Abbot Grimholt (ruled 1484-1517) is recorded to have renovated the church and commissioned a number of pictures for it, among them those by Jan Joest for the high altar.[14] It is reasonable to suppose that the two wings were painted at the same period.[15]

Since studio work is obvious on at least the outside wings, the pictures are catalogued as above. However, No. 252 has every claim to be considered an original picture by the hand of the Master himself.

PROVENANCE: From the abbey at Werden, suppressed in 1803.[16] Passed into the Krüger Collection, Minden, by 1847.[17] Purchased with the majority of the Krüger Collection, 1854. No. 252 on loan to the National Gallery of Scotland, Edinburgh, 1862–1906.

REPRODUCTION: (No. 252) *Illustrations, Continental Schools*, 1937, p. 223.

REFERENCES: (1) See his article in *The Burlington Magazine*, XLIII, 1923, p. 298. (2) For the picture, and some discussion of the point, see Martin Davies, *The Earlier Italian Schools* (National Gallery catalogue), 1951, p. 156. (3) Notes on the costume by Stella M. Pearce in the Gallery archives. (4) Cf. *Vies des Saints* (Petits Bollandistes), XIII, 1882, pp. 127–8. (5) The original high altar, later destroyed, had paintings by Jan Joest, commissioned in 1512: cf. P. Clemen, *Die Kunstdenkmäler* . . . *Essen*, 1893, p. 94. (6) The name used for the first time apparently by E. Förster in *Kunst-Blatt*, 1847, p. 23. (7) Crowe and Cavalcaselle, *Les Anciens Peintres Flamands*, II, 1863, p. 99. (8) H. Brockmann, *Die Spätzeit der Kölner Malerschule*, 1924, p. 302, note 273. (9) A. Stange, *Deutsche Malerei* . . . : V, *Köln in der Zeit von 1450 bis 1515*, 1952, p. 51. The present writer has not consulted Ewald in *Die Pfarre und Kirche St. Cunibert in Köln* (*Festschrift Ditges*), 1911, p. 68, which is cited by Stange, *loc. cit.* (10) His views, given orally in 1932, are recorded in the Gallery archives. (11) Their views are quoted by H. Reiners, *Die Kölner Malerschule*, 1925, p. 310, note 104. See L. Scheibler, *Die hervorragendsten anonymen Meister und Werke der Kölner Malerschule von 1460 bis 1500*, 1880, pp. 33–4, also C. Aldenhoven, *Geschichte der Kölner Malerschule*, 1902, pp. 223–4 and E. Firmenich-Richartz' ed. of Merlo's *Kölnische Künstler*, 1895, col. 1161. (12) Reiners, *op. cit.*, p. 136. (13) See the Wallraf-Richartz Museum *Catalogue*, 1957, p. 34, nos. 129–34; Stange, *op. cit.*, p. 35 and pls. 56–7. (14) See the passage cited by C. P. Baudisch, *Jan Joest von Kalkar*, 1940, p. 190 from *Insignis Monasterii Ludgeri . . . annales*, referring to Grimholt: '. . . ecclesiam artificiosis picturis, exornavit nullis parcens sumptibus'. A date of 1474–8 was accepted tentatively by Aldenhoven, *op. cit.*, p. 224, on the suggestion of L. Gisbertz, *Beiträge zur Geschichte des Stiftes Werden*, 1898, vii, pp. 70 ff., but this seems too early from every point of view. (15) S. M. Pearce draws attention to a slight costume detail in No. 253 (*i.e.* the other wing); the clothes of the man holding a book, just behind S. Hubert, suggest a date in the 1480's. (16) This seems the official date, though the process had begun in 1802. Apart from those objects required for the celebration of mass, all movable things, including pictures, were apparently taken over by the Prussian authorities and presumably afterwards sold; for details of the suppression of Werden, see F. Körholz in *Münstersche Beiträge zur Geschichtsforschung*, 1907, pp. 31 ff. (17) Förster, *loc. cit.*, Krüger catalogue, 1848, Part I, nos. 26–9.

MASTER OF THE LONDON 'THRONE OF MERCY'
Active first half of the XV century

He is named after No. 3662, Austrian School, of this catalogue. A very few other pictures have been ascribed to the same hand,[1] but are not accepted by all scholars. There is close relationship with the Master of S. Lambrecht (who is sometimes identified with Hans von Tübingen[2]), active at S. Lambrecht in Styria. If correctly identified with Hans von Tübingen, the S. Lambrecht Master was active, chiefly at Wiener Neustadt, 1433–62. This period would anyway seem much too late for the author of No. 3662.

In the Austrian exhibition at Geneva, 1950, the London Master was treated as a separate personality and equipped with a complete biography of dates and apprenticeships seemingly documented but entirely suppositous.[3] There is an entry for him in Thieme-Becker *Lexikon*, XXXVII.

REFERENCES: (1) See the discussion in K. Oettinger, *Hans von Tübingen und seine Schule*, 1938, pp. 69 ff. (2) Proposed by K. Oettinger first in Vienna *Jahrbuch*, 1934, pp. 29 ff.; for the documents relating to Hans von Tübingen's activity, Oettinger, *loc. cit.*, pp. 59 ff. For some cautionary words on the subject of this identification, see L. Baldass in *Wiener Jahrbuch für Kunstgeschichte* 1953, p. 9, note 7. (3) See the catalogue *L'Art du Moyen Âge en Autriche*, Geneva, 1950,

p. 50 (no. 98). The attribution of the picture in question, *Madonna and Child in a glory, with angels*, to the hand of No. 3662, was apparently accepted by G. Ring in her review of the exhibition, cf. *The Burlington Magazine*, XCII, 1950, p. 342; it is rejected by Baldass, *loc. cit.*, p. 10, note 9.

See AUSTRIAN SCHOOL, XV century, No. 3662

MASTER OF THE S. BARTHOLOMEW ALTARPIECE
Active late XV/early XVI century

He is named from an altarpiece formerly in S. Columba's, Cologne (now at Munich). At one time the Master was called of the *S. Thomas altar* or 'Master of the Cologne Crucifixion' after two altarpieces by the same hand, at Cologne; originally all these pictures were supposed to be by Lucas van Leyden.

The two altarpieces still at Cologne were apparently commissioned by Dr. Peter Rinck (†1501) for the Carthusian monastery there. The usual interpretation of the documents, such as they are, is that the S. Thomas altar was finished before his death but that the Crucifixion altar was not then finished[1]; Rinck's coat-of-arms appears on the S. Thomas altar but not on the Crucifixion altar. Many of the pictures grouped with the Bartholomew Master are probably well before 1500; some of them, such as the Munich altarpiece, are probably later. The Munich altarpiece is generally accepted as very late work, either of *ca.* 1505–10 or even as after 1510. In addition to religious pictures, some portraits have been attributed to the Master.[2]

The Bartholomew Master was active at Cologne, but there is considerable Netherlandish influence in his work and a relationship specifically with the Utrecht School.[3]

Attempts have been made at various times to identify the Bartholomew Master with painters recorded at Cologne.[4] He was thus at one time supposed to be *Meister Christoph* or *Christophsen*, with whom Petrus Christus was also confused; an altarpiece (now lost) was painted in 1471 by Meister Christoph for the Carthusian monastery at Cologne but there is nothing otherwise to connect this painter with the Bartholomew Master.

REFERENCES: *General:* K. vom Rath, *Der Meister des Bartholomäusaltares*, 1941.

In text: (1) This is the interpretation accepted by vom Rath, *op. cit.*, and by A. Stange, *Deutsche Malerei . . . :* V, *Köln in der Zeit von 1450 bis 1515*, 1952, pp. 67 ff.; see also C. Aldenhoven, *Geschichte der Kölner Malerschule*, 1902, p. 421, note 450. Recently the dating of the two altarpieces has been reversed by P. Pieper, *Wallraf-Richartz Jahrbuch*, 1953, pp. 152 ff. (2) A *Portrait of a Man* (Mortimer coll. New York) which includes a view of the Cathedral at Utrecht was published as by him, by Friedländer, *Wallraf-Richartz Jahrbuch*, 1926–7, p. 176; Friedländer also ascribed to him a *Portrait of Hans Leyckmann(?)* (at Munich) which bears dates *1462* and *1492*: *loc. cit.*, p. 182, note 2. Vom Rath puts the first of these among School work (his cat. no. 25) and rejects the second, *loc. cit.*, pp. 96–7. Both are accepted by E. Buchner, *Das deutsche Bildnis der Spätgotik und der frühen Dürerzeit*, 1953, nos. 15 and 16. A portrait of *Walther von Rottkirchen* (dated 1479, but surviving only in a later copy) is accepted at least as School work by vom Rath (his no. 27) but rejected by Buchner, *op. cit.*, no. 12. Stange, *op. cit.*, pp. 64 and 70–1 accepts all three. (3) See especially G. Ring in *Oud-Holland*, 1939, pp. 26 ff.; H. Busch in *Konsthistorisk Tidskrift*, 1939, pp. 33 ff.; and P. Pieper in *Wallraf-Richartz Jahrbuch*, 1953, pp. 154 ff. (4) Vom Rath, *op. cit.*, pp. 7 ff., gives a list of fifteen candidates.

707 SS. PETER AND DOROTHY

Verso: S. John the Evangelist and the Virgin and Child.

S. Peter with the keys; in his left hand a pair of spectacles. S. Dorothy holding a basket of flowers. S. John holding a chalice with a serpent.

Oak, *recto*, painted surface, $49\frac{1}{2} \times 28$ ($1\cdot255 \times 71$); *verso*, painted surface, $49\frac{1}{4} \times 27\frac{1}{2}$ ($1\cdot25 \times 0\cdot695$).

In very good condition; a few minor damages and retouchings, S. Dorothy's face being most obviously affected. A certain amount of flaking on the *verso*.

For S. Dorothy. see under No. 2152, Circle of the Master of Liesborn. Another depiction of her by the Bartholomew Master is in the *Baptism of Christ* (Kress collection).

No. 717 is the left wing of an altarpiece of which the right wing is at Mainz. On that *recto* are shown SS. Andrew and Columba[1]; *verso*,[2] two kings, bearing gifts, apparently adoring the Virgin and Child on the *verso* of No. 707. Vom Rath has associated with these wings two fragments, a head of S. James and a head of the Virgin, which he thinks might be from the destroyed central panel.[3] Since S. Columba appears on the Mainz wing it is possible that the pictures came from S. Columba's at Cologne[4] where the Master painted other altarpieces (referred to in the biography above).

The *verso* of No. 707 is journey work, possibly derived in design from the same two figures on the Master's Munich altarpiece. In No. 707 the Child is blessing the two kings in adoration on the *verso* of the Mainz panel. According to Aldenhoven the *versi* are by a pupil influenced by the Master of the Holy Kindred.[5]

The London/Mainz wings are closely related in style to the Master's *S. Bartholomew altar* at Munich and are therefore late work.[6] As has been indicated in the biography above, a firm date for the Munich altar cannot be given but it must originate approximately in the first decade of the sixteenth century.

PROVENANCE: No. 707 apparently separated from the rest of its altar by 1688 when valued.[7] Count Joseph von Rechberg collection, Mindelheim,[8] whence bought in 1815 by Prince Ludwig Kraft Ernst von Oettingen-Wallerstein.[9] At Schloss Wallerstein.[10] Exhibited for sale at Kensington Palace, 1848 (no. 67), bought with the rest of the collection by the Prince Consort. At Kensington Palace.[11] Exhibited at Manchester, 1857 (Provisional Catalogue, no. 440; Definitive Catalogue, no. 441), lent by Prince Albert. Presented by Queen Victoria, at the Prince Consort's wish, 1863.[12]

REPRODUCTION: *Illustrations, Continental Schools*, 1937, p. 210 (*recto*). M. Davies, *Paintings and Drawings on the backs of National Gallery Pictures*, 1946, pl. 16 (*verso*).

REFERENCES: (1) The *recto* reproduced by K. vom Rath, *Der Meister des Bartholomäusaltares*, 1941, fig. 38. (2) First commented on by L. Scheibler in *Repertorium für Kunstwissenschaft*, 1884, p. 54. The picture has not apparently been reproduced, and the present writer is indebted to Dr. Esser for a photograph. The two kings are shown against a patterned curtain, and on a chequered floor, similar to the curtain and floor on the *verso* of No. 707. (3) Vom Rath, *op. cit.*, pp. 88–9; also the same author in Thieme-Becker *Lexikon*, XXXVII, *ad vocem*. (4) This suggestion had already been made by Martin Davies, and is made again by vom Rath, *op. cit.*, p. 88, who notes, however, that research into S. Columba's archives has been unsuccessful in establishing this. (5) C. Aldenhoven, *Geschichte der Kölner Malerschule*, 1902, pp. 270–1. (6) Cf. Aldenhoven, *op. cit.*, p. 271; later than the London/Mainz wings he puts only the Louvre *Deposition*. For the late dating, see also A. Stange, *Deutsche Malerei* . . . : V, *Köln in der Zeit von 1450 bis 1515*, 1952, pp. 69–70, mentioning further fragments possibly from the altarpiece of which No. 707 was part. (7) According to the 1913 Gallery catalogue there was an inscription [*sic*] on No. 707 reading: 'Dis bild ist umb fünffhundert gulden estimiert von mir aber nachmals umb 105 fl. bezihit. 1688 zi. 8 brl.' No trace of this remains today and the fact does not seem otherwise recorded; some comment on it is in vom Rath, *op. cit.*, pp. 87–8. (8) According to the National Gallery MS. catalogue, No. 707 is ex-Boisserée but there seems no other record of this and it is perhaps a mistake. (9) See *Kunst-Blatt*, 1824, pp. 318 (No. 707 as Lucas van Leyden) and 353. (10) 1826(?) lithographed catalogue, no. 63, Lucas van Leyden, *SS. Peter and Rosalia*; 1827 MS. catalogue, same number, attribution and title, with a note of the Mainz wing. (11) Waagen's *Catalogue*, 1854 (no. 46) as Cologne School, supposed to be by Meister Christoph (cf. the biography above). (12) As by the Master of the Cologne Crucifixion (cf. the biography above).

MASTER OF THE S. URSULA LEGEND
Active late XV/early XVI century

He was first named by Aldenhoven after a scattered series of scenes from the life of S. Ursula previously associated with the Master of S. Severin.[1] The creation of this personality did not go uncontested but the tendency is now to accept that these pictures, with some others, are by a distinct hand.[2] There is obvious inter-relation between the two groups, and the style is common to pictures of the Cologne School at the turn of the fifteenth century (*vide* Master of the Aachen Altarpiece).

Brockmann developed Aldenhoven's creation more fully,[3] but his proposal that the S. Ursula Master was later than the Master of S. Severin is not accepted by, for instance, Stange.[4]

The Master of the S. Ursula Legend was apparently active at Cologne, but the Dutch influences in his work suggest that possibly he was trained in Holland. The earliest work attributed to him by Stange probably dates from about 1480.

REFERENCES: (1) C. Aldenhoven, *Geschichte der Kölner Malerschule*, 1902, pp. 293 ff. (2) For the literature on both sides, cf. A. Stange, *Deutsche Malerei* . . . V: *Köln in der Zeit von 1450 bis 1515*, 1952, p. 92, note 2. (3) H. Brockmann, *Die Spätzeit der Kölner Malerschule*, 1924. (4) *Loc. cit.* On this point see also the comments of H. W. Hupp when reviewing Brockmann in *Repertorium für Kunstwissenschaft*, 1926, pp. 114 ff.

Circle of the MASTER OF THE S. URSULA LEGEND

3665 S. LAWRENCE SHOWING THE PREFECT THE TREASURES OF THE CHURCH

At the left S. Lawrence and the Prefect; at the right the poor.

Canvas, $51\frac{1}{4} \times 36\frac{1}{2}$ (1·302 × 0·927).

In fair condition under discoloured varnish; but there is general wearing and some repainted damages in the right-hand portion of the picture, also in the background buildings and the sky.

S. Lawrence was commanded by the Prefect Decius to reveal the treasures of the Church. He assembed the poor of Rome and showed them to the Prefect, declaring they were the treasures of the Church.[1]

No. 3665 was presented as of the Dutch School and it was so catalogued in 1929. Its relationship to the Cologne Master of S. Ursula was first postulated by Brockmann. He pointed out that it belongs with other pictures in a S. Lawrence cycle and mentioned another five pictures from the cycle, implying that probably there were originally eight.[2] Stange speaks of seven pictures surviving, including No. 3665, but this seems to be a mistake.[3] Some of these pictures bear coats-of-arms which may have been added later; nothing seems known of how the series was originally arranged or what church it comes from.

The series was at first associated with the Master of S. Severin but was by Brockmann given to the following of the S. Ursula Master.[4] He dated it about 1510. It has been denied that the series is anything to do with the S. Ursula Master,[5] but Stange has recently followed Brockmann's ascription[6] which seems to the present writer the correct one. It is not clear whether the S. Lawrence cycle is really by a separate hand or whether it might not come from the S. Ursula Master's studio. No. 3665 seems to the present writer quite close to pictures accepted as from the Master's own hand.

PROVENANCE: From the Schwarzschild collection, Warsaw. By 1892 in the collection of Charles Roberts, London.[7] Lent by Sir Henry Howorth to the New Gallery exhibition 1899–1900 (no. 245).[8] Presented by Sir Henry Howorth, through the National Art-Collections Fund, in memory of Lady Howorth, 1922.

REPRODUCTION: Illustrations, Continental Schools, 1937, p. 98.

REFERENCES: General: H. Brockmann in The Burlington Magazine, LI, 1927, pp. 133–4.

In text: (1) Cf. the life, derived from the Flos Sanctorum, in A. Jameson, Sacred and Legendary Art, 1850 ed., pp. 320 ff. (2) In addition to No. 3665, Brockmann names and reproduces: S. Lawrence exchanged at birth for a monster; S. Lawrence distributing treasure to the poor; Condemnation of S. Lawrence (all Wallraf-Richartz Museum, Cologne); S. Lawrence baptises his jailer (Neisser Coll., Berlin); Martyrdom of S. Lawrence (Berlin dealer in the 1920's). (3) A. Stange, Deutsche Malerei . . . V: Köln in der Zeit von 1450 bis 1515, 1952, p. 115, apparently referring for the seventh to P. Wescher in Pantheon, 1933, p. 25, who mentions a Burial of S. Lawrence then at Van Diemen's, Berlin. Wescher's reference is misleading, for the burial of S. Lawrence is shown in the background of the Martyrdom reproduced by Brockmann, loc. cit. It therefore seems reasonable to suppose that the two pictures are really the same. An annotation in the National Gallery copy of *The Burlington Magazine* records this picture as in the Barnes Foundation, Philadelphia. (4) H. Brockmann, *Die Spätzeit der Kölner Malerschule*, 1924, pp. 201 ff., also pp. 269–70. (5) Cf. the entry for the S. Ursula Master in Thieme-Becker *Lexikon*, XXXVII. (6) Stange, *loc. cit.* (7) Letter from the then owner, with previous provenance, in the Gallery archives; the picture then said to be by 'Dirk Stuerbout' (*i.e.* Bouts). (8) As Flemish School.

MASTER OF S. VERONICA
Active early XV century

He is named from a *S. Veronica with the Sudarium* (at Munich) which comes from the church of S. Severin, Cologne; the Master was presumably active at Cologne. A few other pictures have been grouped as his, among them the *Madonna of the Sweet-Pea* (Nuremberg) and a triptych with central panel of the same subject (Cologne); the latter picture has sometimes been rejected, as being supposedly a Westphalian work.[1] At one time these pictures, along with others, were said to be the work of Master Wilhelm who is recorded in 1380 as the 'best painter in Germany'.[2] No picture by Master Wilhelm survives, and there is now general agreement that his activity is anyway too early for him to be the Veronica Master. Firmenich-Richartz introduced into the discussion Hermann Wynrich von Wesel (apparently died 1413/14), a pupil of Master Wilhelm's, who he thought might be the Veronica Master but—apart from anything else—the date of his death would probably exclude him.[3] The names of a number of other painters of the period at Cologne are recorded, but it is not possible to link any of them convincingly with the anonymous Master.

REFERENCES : *General:* K. H. Schweitzer, *Der Veronikameister und sein Kreis*, 1935.

In text: (1) It was in fact published by F. Witte in *Zeitschrift für christliche Kunst*, 1921, pp. 75 ff., as by Conrad von Soest; in the exhibition *Conrad von Soest*, Cappenberg (Dortmund), 1950, no. 112 ff. as by a Cologne painter, *ca.* 1420. In the 1957 Wallraf-Richartz Museum catalogue still as by the Veronica Master. For some discussion of the attribution of these two Madonna pictures, see A Stange, *Deutsche Malerei . . .* : III, *Norddeutschland in der Zeit von 1400 bis 1450*, 1938, pp. 59 ff. The Cologne picture is said to be rejected by most modern scholars, in Thieme-Becker *Lexikon*, XXXVII (under the Veronica Master). (2) In the Limburg Chronicle; Schweitzer, *op. cit.*, p. 8. (3) See E. Firmenich-Richartz in *Zeitschrift für christliche Kunst*, 1895, cols. 97 ff., 129 ff., 233 ff., 297 ff., 320 ff. The objections put by Schweitzer, *op. cit.*, pp. 9 ff.

Circle of the MASTER OF S. VERONICA

687 S. VERONICA WITH THE SUDARIUM

Incised in the gold ground on either side of S. Veronica are traces of drapery (?) and wings, probably of adoring angels.[1]

S. Veronica's halo inscribed: *sancta. veronica.* Christ's halo inscribed: *ihs. xps. ihs. x.*

Walnut, painted area, $17\frac{3}{8} \times 13\frac{1}{4}$ (0·442 × 0·337).

In quite good condition under discoloured varnish, although the gold background is damaged and repainted.

The attribution of No. 687 has always been dependent on the Munich *S. Veronica*, and it has previously been catalogued as by or ascribed to Master Wilhelm or to Hermann Wynrich von Wesel (for both of whom, see the biography above). E. Firmenich-Richartz originally thought the picture by an immediate follower of Hermann Wynrich[2]; later he attributed it to the Master of S. Lawrence, a personality he created out of some pictures closely associable with the Veronica Master.[3] Reiners recognized the association of No. 687 with the Veronica Master but attributed the picture simply to the Cologne School, *ca.* 1400.[4] Stange has inclined to see in No. 687 a workshop repetition.[5]

The present writer thinks Stange's view quite possibly the correct one. The handling of No. 687 is quite close to that of the Munich picture, even if the latter is granted to be of higher quality. Where however so little is established about the Master, it seems best at present to catalogue the picture no more exactly than above, especially as the Master is such a doubtful personality. There is no doubt that the picture is typical of Cologne School work early in the fifteenth century.

It should perhaps be emphasized that No. 687 is rather intentionally different in effect from the Munich picture, as Hotho long ago remarked.[6] The image of Christ in No. 687 is not as Man of Sorrows; He is not shown with the Crown of Thorns.

E. Weyden had a theory that the red and green of S. Veronica's robe in No. 687 might be an indication that the picture had been painted for the Overstolzen family who alone had the privilege of wearing a comparably coloured cloak.[7]

PROVENANCE: From the church of S. Lawrence, Cologne (demolished in 1817). Later in the hands of a priest whence it passed to the Cologne dealer, Spanner.[8] Acquired from him by Johann Peter Weyer by 1851 [9]; Weyer sale, 25 August 1862 (lot 116)[10] bought by O. Mündler for the National Gallery.

REPRODUCTION: *Illustrations, Continental Schools*, 1937, p. 404.

REFERENCES: (1) Repaint obscures these figures and attempts by photography to discover more about them have been only partly successful. They were identified as praying angels by E. Weyden, see his article cited in the note 7 below, at a time when perhaps they were more visible. (2) See *Zeitschrift für christliche Kunst*, 1895, col. 338. (3) See his article on the S. Lawrence Master in *Zeitschrift für christliche Kunst*, 1910, col. 329. Firmenich-Richartz' creation has not been widely taken up in scholarship, and it is doubtful if there is an individual hand on the pictures he grouped as by the S. Lawrence Master; on the point in general, cf. Schweitzer, *op. cit.*, pp. 59 ff., and Stange, *op. cit.*, pp. 65 ff. (4) H. Reiners, *Die Kölner Malerschule*, 1925, p. 32 and fig. 22. (5) *Op. cit.*, p. 64. (6) Cf. his comment in *Die Malerschule Huberts van Eyck*, 1855, I, p. 244. (7) See his article on No. 687 in *Deutsches Kunst-blatt*, 1851, pp. 4–5. His theory would also apply, though he does not say so, to the Munich picture. (8) The provenance is given by W. H. J. Weale in *Messager des Sciences Historiques de Belgique*, 1862, pp. 343–4 (his notice of the Weyer collection). In Weale's opinion No. 687 was superior in quality to the Munich picture. (9) When published by E. Weyden, *loc. cit.* (10) As by Master Wilhelm.

ANTON RAPHAEL MENGS
1728–1779

Born at Aussig, Bohemia, 12 March 1728. He was the son of the painter, Ismael Mengs, by whom he was trained while still very young. He visited Rome[1] first in 1741 and remained there until 1744. In 1745 he was made court painter at Dresden to the Elector Augustus II of Saxony. He was again in Rome 1747–9 and 1752–61. In 1761 he was summoned to Madrid by Charles III and remained there until early in 1771, returning to Rome chiefly through ill-health. He was at Madrid again 1773–7. Died at Rome, 29 June 1779.

Mengs' very early pictures were pastel portraits and copies after the Old Masters, Raphael above all. The arrival of Winckelmann in Rome in 1755 was probably decisive in making a neo-classic painter of him.[2] He completed the *Parnassus* ceiling of Villa Albani, Rome, in 1761. In Spain he painted altarpieces for Aranjuez (replacing those of Tiepolo) and frescoes in the Royal Palace at Madrid, as well as portraits. For All Souls' Chapel at Oxford he painted in 1771 a large *Noli Me Tangere* altarpiece[3] and in general was considerably patronized by the English.

REFERENCES : (1) For the correct dates of Mengs' stays in Rome, see F. Noack, *Das Deutschtum in Rom* . . . , 1927, II, p. 393. A drawing in the British Museum, signed and dated 'a Roma 1741'. (2) For recent discussion on this point, see E. K. Waterhouse, *The British Contribution to the Neo-Classical Style in Painting* (British Academy Lecture), 1954. (3) C. G. Ratti, *Epilogo della vita del fu Cavaliere Antonio Raffaello Mengs*, 1779, p. vii; the exact date given by G. L. Bianconi, *Elogio Storico del cavaliere Anton Raffaele Mengs*, 1780, p. 52. The picture survives at All Souls'.

1099 THE VIRGIN AND CHILD WITH THE INFANT S. JOHN

Paper, crayoned area a tondo, 27⅛ diameter (0·689).

In good condition, though slightly rubbed; one or two small tears in the paper.

The drawing was probably quite early mounted on canvas, on the back of which is written *Mengs* but this is not a signature.

Mengs executed a number of highly finished black crayon drawings, intended as works of art in their own right.[1] No. 1099 is clearly one of these and is not preparatory to any painting of the subject. Some of these drawings were engraved, but not apparently No. 1099.

The Raphaelesque air of the composition is obvious, but the group of Virgin and sleeping Child seems closely derived from Sassoferrato. The drawing was catalogued in 1929 only as ascribed to Mengs, but there is no reason to doubt that it is by him.

PROVENANCE: Bequeathed by Miss Harriet Kearsley, 1881.

REPRODUCTION: *Bryan's Dictionary of Painters and Engravers*, III, 1904, facing p. 322.

REFERENCE : (1) Cf. the comments of his pupil C. G. Ratti, *Epilogo della vita del fu Cavaliere Antonio Raffaello Mengs*, 1779, p. xxix.

NORTH GERMAN School

2160 CHRIST CARRYING THE CROSS

Oak, painted surface, $16\frac{7}{8} \times 11\frac{1}{2}$ (0·429 × 0·292) within an apparently original gold moulding; arched top.

In quite good condition, though somewhat damaged in the faces.

No. 2160 entered the collection as German School. In the 1929 catalogue as Westphalian, which is far from certain. The picture seems North German in origin; the style suggests Lübeck work. It is perhaps part of a series of Christ's Passion, but the present writer has not traced any pictures which might be related. It probably dates from very late in the fifteenth century or early in the sixteenth century.

PROVENANCE: In the Krüger collection, Minden, by 1848.[1] Bought with the majority of the collection, 1854. On loan to the National Gallery of Ireland, Dublin, 1857–1926.

REPRODUCTION: A negative exists at the National Gallery.

REFERENCE: (1) Krüger catalogue, 1848, Part II, no. 13, as by an unknown master.

MICHAEL PACHER

Active 1465(?)–died 1498

An altarpiece, apparently now lost, is recorded to have been inscribed with Pacher's name and the date 1465.[1] He is mentioned as painter and citizen at Bruneck in the Tyrol, from 1467–96.[2] The contract for his altarpiece at Gries, near Bolzano, is dated 27 May 1471, and the altarpiece was probably finished about 1475. The contract for his altarpiece at St. Wolfgang is dated 13 December 1471; the altarpiece was finished by 1481.[3] The altarpiece of the *Four Fathers of the Church* (Munich) for Kloster Neustift is probably of *ca.* 1483. He was active at Salzburg first in 1484 and for considerable portions of the period 1496–8. Many payments to him are recorded for the high altarpiece, surviving only in a few fragments, which was in what is now the Franciscan church there; from these it may be deduced that he was living on 7 July 1498 (last payment to him) but dead by 24 August that year.[4]

Pacher worked as painter and sculptor, the altarpieces commissioned from him usually including pictures and sculpture. Some drawings have been attributed to him. Almost contemporaneously active in the Tyrol were Friedrich and Hans Pacher, but their relationship to Michael, or to each other, is not known.

REFERENCES: *General:* E. Hempel, *Michael Pacher*, 1931.

In text: (1) First referred to, not quite correctly, by A. Woltmann and K. Woermann; cf. *History of Painting* (transl. C. Bell), II, 1885, p. 121. See also Hempel, *op. cit.*, p. 81. H. Semper, *Michael und Friedrich Pacher*, 1911, p. 311, mentions another altar allegedly inscribed and dated 1465. (2) For documents concerning Pacher (with a bibliography of their publication and some cautionary comments) cf. W. Mannowsky, *Pacher*, 1910, pp. 97 ff. (3) The contracts for these two altarpieces printed by Hempel, *op. cit.*, p. 91. (4) On that day payment was made instead to Pacher's son-in-law, Caspar Neuhauser, and again to him on 17 November 1498.

Circle of PACHER

5786 THE VIRGIN AND CHILD ENTHRONED WITH ANGELS AND SAINTS

At the left S. Michael weighing a human soul; right, a bishop saint. On the pillars at either side of the Virgin, the Angel Gabriel and the Virgin annunciate.

On the reverse traces of a red diaper pattern.

Silver fir (*abies alba*), painted surface $15\frac{7}{8} \times 15\frac{1}{2}$ (0.403×0.394).

In general in good condition; the effect is slightly disturbed by cracks.

No. 5786 entered the collection as by Pacher. It was published by Cecil Gould who pointed out its strong affinities with Pacher, while expressing reserve on the attribution and recording German scholars' dissent from the attribution.[1] The picture is certainly dissimilar in handling from what is known of Pacher's work which is usually on much larger scale. It might just conceivably be connected with his early style, if anything of this were established.

It must be admitted that No. 5786 is not in handling very like most of the work in Pacher's following. A suggestion of proximity to the Master of Uttenheim has apparently been made, but the present writer cannot see any close relationship between what is accepted as his and No. 5786.[2] It is possibly by an independent painter influenced by Pacher yet working in a rather different technique. It has been linked with a Madonna and Child fresco on the façade of the parish church at Bolzano,[3] but the status of that damaged work is not very clear. Ringler has discussed the picture in some detail, without, however, being able to come to any certain conclusion; he emphasizes the high quality of No. 5786 and its affinities with Pacher. The heading of this entry is deliberately tentative in the present state of knowledge.

A date in the last quarter of the fifteenth century, and nearer 1475 than 1500, has been suggested by Sir James Mann on the evidence of S. Michael's armour.[4]

PROVENANCE: Acquired by George A. Simonson from an old family near Bolzano, *ca.* 1913–14.[5] Exhibited at the Burlington Fine Arts Club 1932–3 (no. 29).[6] Bequeathed by Miss Anna S. H. Simonson, 1947.

REPRODUCTION: *The Burlington Magazine*, XCIII, 1951, facing p. 369.

REFERENCES: *General*: Cecil Gould in *The Burlington Magazine*, XCIII, 1951, pp. 389–90. J. Ringler in *Der Schlern*, Feb. 1951, pp. 55 ff. (A typescript of this article was very kindly sent by Dr. M. Poch-Kalous, to whom the present writer is much indebted.)

In text: (1) Gould, *loc. cit.* He points out the affinities between No. 5786 and Pacher's sculpture (*e.g.* his statues of S. Michael) and calls the picture a microcosm of Pacher's largest and most important works in painting and sculpture.

(2) For the Uttenheim Master, cf. the exhibition catalogue, *Gotik in Tirol*, Innsbruck, 1950, pp. 41 ff. (3) First by V. Oberhammer, cf. Ringler, *loc. cit.* (4) Letter of 1949 in the Gallery archives. (5) Information from E. K. Waterhouse in the Gallery archives. (6) As by Pacher.

MARTIN SCHONGAUER
Active 1469–died 1491

He was the son of a goldsmith, Caspar Schongauer, of Augsburg family but settled in Colmar by 1445 and acquiring citizenship in that year. The date of Schongauer's birth is not known; the first reference to him is in the matriculation book of Leipzig University, winter term 1465[1]; the inferences to be drawn from this mention of him (and it seems impossible that any other man is meant) are not quite clear. He is mentioned as living at Colmar in 1469, and there are some later references to him there; he never apparently acquired citizenship at Colmar but still retained half a house there in 1490. By the summer of 1489 he was a citizen of Breisach, where he painted frescoes in the cathedral. He died apparently at Breisach, 2 February 1491.

There are some initialled drawings and all Schongauer's engravings are initialled. The *Madonna of the Rose Hedge* (St. Martin's, Colmar) is dated on the back 1473: no paintings by, or attributed to, Schongauer are signed and no other is dated. Dürer dated a Schongauer drawing 1469[2]; he also recorded on another drawing (now lost) that Schongauer executed it in 1470 when he was young.[3] Some evidence for the vexed problem of Schongauer's birth date seems to be provided by a portrait of him at Munich: this bears a date which must apparently be read as 1453.[4] The subject of Schongauer's travels is also obscure; Lambert Lombard told Vasari that Schongauer studied under Rogier van der Weyden (†1465)[5] and he certainly studied Rogier's altarpiece at Beaune.[6] He is sometimes said to have visited Spain.

Schongauer's brothers Caspar, Jörg and Paul, were active as goldsmiths; his brother Ludwig was active as a painter.

REFERENCES: *General:* E. Buchner, *Martin Schongauer als Maler*, 1941. E. Flechsig, *Martin Schongauer*, 1951 ed. J. Baum, *Martin Schongauer*, 1948 (with reprinting of documents and bibliographical references).

In text: (1) The name is given as 'Martinus Schöngawer de Colmar'. Whether Schongauer was studying at the university or whether he matriculated as a painter is not clear; the bearing on his age of this disputed point is obvious. As well as authors cited above, cf. M. Geisberg's comments in Thieme-Becker *Lexikon*, XXX, *ad vocem.* and A. Stange in *Deutsche Malerei der Gotik*: VII, *Oberrhein . . . in der Zeit von 1450 bis 1500*, 1955, p. 19. (2) The drawing is J. Rosenberg, *Martin Schongauer: Handzeichnungen*, 1923, pl. 23. It is a partial copy of Rogier van der Weyden's *Last Judgment* at Beaune. Another drawing (Rosenberg, pl. 37) of the *Saviour* (British Museum) is inscribed by Dürer as done by Schongauer in 1469; it seems probable that this drawing is not by Schongauer but is copied from him by Dürer himself. (3) This drawing belonged to Heinecken in the eighteenth century and he carefully recorded Dürer's inscription on it. In conjunction with the Leipzig reference (however explained) Dürer's reference to Schongauer as young in 1470 seems ground for not pushing Schongauer's date of birth too far back into the twenties. (4) See the discussion of this picture by E. Buchner, *Beiträge zur Geschichte der deutschen Kunst*, II, 1928, pp. 16 ff., and especially the same author, *Das deutsche Bildnis der Spätgotik und der frühen Dürerzeit*, 1953, pl. 56 and pp. 67 ff., publishing X-ray photographs of the picture. Flechsig, *op. cit.*, pp. 1 ff., strongly argues for 1483. See also the discussion in J. Baum, *op. cit.*, pp. 10 ff. (5) Quoted in Baum, *op. cit.*, p. 67. (6) See the note 2 above.

Style of SCHONGAUER

723 THE VIRGIN AND CHILD IN A GARDEN

Lime, painted surface, $11\frac{7}{8} \times 8\frac{5}{8}$ (0·302 × 0·219).

In quite good condition under discoloured varnish; a vertical crack right of the Virgin extends the height of the panel.

The subject was particularly popular in Alsace.[1] Most of the flowers in No. 723 seem to have no particular significance, except for the iris at the right which is often introduced as a symbol of Christ's Passion.[2]

The picture was catalogued in 1929 as 'School of Schongauer'; earlier it had been catalogued as by Schongauer, the relation to whom was first made by Waagen.[3] Lippmann called it a late copy 'after the print'.[4] In fact, the composition of No. 723 is quite close to a Schongauer engraving (Bartsch 30) but in no sense a copy of that engraving. A drawing by Schongauer at Berlin shows a somewhat similarly posed Virgin and Child on a grass bank but is again rather different in detail from No. 723.[5]

Buchner thinks the picture likely to be a copy, possibly after a lost original by Schongauer.[6] He rightly comments on the stylization of the plants. Baum has accepted the picture as either the copy of a lost original or a studio piece, and the latter is conceivable.[7] No. 723 certainly seems an old picture and not merely a later copy or pastiche, though its quality is hardly high enough to attribute it to Schongauer himself.

PROVENANCE: In the Prince Ludwig Kraft Ernst von Oettingen-Wallerstein collection.[8] Exhibited for sale at Kensington Palace, 1848 (no. 39),[9] bought with. the rest of the collection by the Prince Consort; at Kensington Palace, 1854.[10] Exhibited at Manchester, 1857 (Provisional Catalogue no. 441; Definitive Catalogue no. 437) lent by Prince Albert. Presented by Queen Victoria at the Prince Consort's wish, 1863.

REPRODUCTION: *Illustrations, Continental Schools*, 1937, p. 336.

REFERENCES: (1) See the discussion in H. Haug, *Martin Schongauer et Hans Burgkmair*, 1938, pp. 11 ff. (2) Compare the comment under No. 5592 of this catalogue, Style of Dürer. (3) In his catalogue of the Kensington Palace pictures, 1854, no. 30; see further under Provenance. (4) Letter in *The Burlington Magazine*, XII, 1907–8, p. 108. (5) For the Berlin drawing cf. J. Rosenberg, *Martin Schongauer: Handzeichnungen*, 1923, pl. 24 (the engraving, *op. cit.*, pl. 25) and his discussion, pp. 27–8. (6) E. Buchner, *Martin Schongauer als Maler*, 1941, pp. 100–1; see also his p. 184. (7) J. Baum, *Martin Schongauer*, 1948, fig. 195 and pp. 59–60. (8) The present writer has not succeeded in tracing No. 723 in the Schloss Wallerstein catalogues of 1826 and 1827. (9) As School of Dürer. (10) When attributed by Waagen to Schongauer (see the note 3 above). See also Waagen, *Galleries and Cabinets of Art . . .*, IV, 1857, p. 255.

Heinrich Wilhelm SCHWEICKHARDT
1746–1797

Or *Schweickardt*, but the form above is that more commonly used by the painter. Born at Brandenburg. He is said to have been a pupil of Hieronymus Lapis at The Hague. He was in The Hague by June 1774, when he made his will.[1] He remained active there until 1787 in which year he settled in London.[2] He had previously visited England in 1786[3] when he first exhibited at the Royal Academy. In 1788 he published *Eight Etchings of Animals* . . . (dedicated to Benjamin West, who is said to have patronized him). From 1786 onwards he exhibited most years at the Academy and in 1790 at the Society of Artists. Died in London, 8 July 1797.

Among the earliest known dated works are two *Flower-pieces* of 1771.[4] Schweickhardt painted chiefly landscapes with cattle and scenes on the ice, usually pastiches of Dutch seventeenth-century artists. One or two portraits are recorded[5] and one or two views in the grounds of English houses. A considerable amount of his work was in the H. W. Schweickhardt sale, London, 8–10 June 1799. His daughter Katharina (1777–1830) worked as a flower painter in Holland.

REFERENCES: (1) Published by A. Bredius, *Oud-Holland* (LV) 1938, p. 37. (2) See A. Bredius' publication of extracts from the 'Pictura' guild records, in *Oud Holland* (XIX), 1901, p. 236, under date 9 May 1787. (3) Bredius, *op. cit.*, 1901, p. 235, under 22 April 1786. (4) Cf. A. von Wurzbach, *Niederländisches Künstler-Lexikon*, 1910 (*ad vocem*). (5) Compare for example R.A. 1791 (no. 9) *Portrait of a Young Lady*.

1878 CATTLE

A view of a river at the left.
Signed, bottom right, *H. W. Schweickhardt f. 1794.*
Oil on mahogany, $18\frac{1}{4} \times 24$ (0·464 × 0·61).
In very good condition.

No. 1878 is typical of Schweickhardt's pastiches in the manner of Cuyp and Potter.

PROVENANCE: Perhaps the *Cattle* exhibited by the painter at the Royal Academy in the year the picture is dated, 1794 (no. 316).[1] Mrs. S. F. Hodges Bequest, 1852. From 1895–1929 on loan to Blackburn Art Gallery.

REPRODUCTION: *Illustrations, Continental Schools*, 1937, p. 337.

REFERENCE: (1) Conceivably in the Schweickhardt sale, 8 June 1799 (lot 81). *Cows with a view of a river*—but the title could obviously apply to a number of Schweickhardt's pictures.

Jakob SEISENEGGER
1504/5–1567

Alternative spellings of the name occur. The date of birth is from a medal of Seisenegger by Mathes Gebel (of 1543)[1]; the place of birth is not known but was probably somewhere in Austria. In 1531 he was made court painter to the Emperor Ferdinand I at Augsburg; the following year he was at Innsbruck and at Bologna where he painted a full length portrait of the Emperor Charles V (Vienna; monogram and date 1532).[2] In the years 1535–45 he travelled to Vienna and Prague, and visited also Spain and the Netherlands; in 1540 he is recorded at Augsburg.[3] In 1550 he acquired a house at Vienna. In 1561 he settled at Linz, where he died.

Seisenegger painted a few religious pictures, but chiefly portraits, and was considerably patronized by the Habsburg family.

REFERENCES: (1) Cf. G. Habich, *Die deutschen Schaumünzen des XVI Jahrhunderts*, I (2nd part), 1931, no. 1224. (2) For the influence of this portrait on Titian, see the dialogue devised by G. Glück in *Festschrift für Julius Schlosser*, 1927, pp. 224 ff. Some further comment on the influence of Seisenegger in general by E. Auerbach, *The Burlington Magazine*, XCI, 1949, pp. 218 ff. (3) See the biography of him in the exhibition catalogue *Augsburger Renaissance*, Augsburg, 1955, p. 79.

4206   PORTRAIT ,OF A GIRL

Nearly full face, to the left.

Oak, painted up to the edges all round, $11\frac{3}{8} \times 8\frac{1}{2}$ (0·289 × 0·216); almost certainly cut down all round.

There are a few small repainted damages and some wearing. The shadow of the caul at the right is new. A *pentimento* in the outline of the cap. A fake Cranach device at the left is revealed by X-ray photography.

The costume of the sitter, in conjunction with Seisenegger's usual employment, suggests that the girl is of a princely family. The size of No. 4206 is unusually small for Seisenegger and it is likely to be the head cut from a rather larger portrait.[1]

The picture is first recorded in the nineteenth century in the Abel collection at Stuttgart (see under Provenance); and it passed to the Gemäldegalerie, Stuttgart, where it was retained until 1925. Through the kindness of Dr. B. Bushart[2] it has been possible to trace in some detail the various attributions of the picture and its other adventures. The fake Cranach device helps to explain its earliest known attribution, to Lucas Cranach the Younger. At a later date it was called School of Holbein the Younger; and later still was supposed to be a copy after Holbein.

In the nineteenth century, the sitter was identified as a princess of Saxony on account of a medal with the Saxon electoral coat-of-arms which hung from the chain about her neck. This portion of the picture was, as Lange pointed out, a later addition by another hand[3]; and additions had also been made at the sides.[4] These additions seem to have been removed by 1926. Lange doubtfully supposed the sitter to be English.

The correct attribution was first made by Frimmel.[5] The picture has been dated by K. Rathe *ca.* 1535–40[6] but the costume suggests a rather later period, *ca.* 1545–50.[7]

PROVENANCE: In the Abel collection, Stuttgart, and exhibited with the rest of the collection at Schloss Ludwigsburg, 1855 (no. 37).[8] Among the Abel pictures bought by the King of Würtemburg in 1859. In the Stuttgart Museum catalogue, 1891 (no. 500)[9]; 1907 catalogue (12 Cc.)[10]; 1917 catalogue (no. 12).[11] Exchanged with Böhler, Munich, 1925.[12] Bought by the National Art-Collections Fund and presented, 1926.

REPRODUCTION: *Illustrations, Continental Schools*, 1937, p. 338.

REFERENCES: (1) Compare for instance the portraits by him of Habsburg children at The Hague. (2) Letter of 1959 in the Gallery archives; the present writer is indebted to Dr. Bushart for the trouble he has taken in tracing earlier records of No. 4206. (3) Cf. his Stuttgart catalogue of 1907, p. 50, under no. 12 Cc. Copy after(?) Holbein the Younger. (4) A photograph of the picture with all these additions kindly sent by Dr. Bushart, in the Gallery archives. (5) T. von Frimmel in *Blätter für Gemäldekunde*, III, 1907, p. 114; Frimmel's attribution recorded in Lange's Appendix, p. 286 to his 1907 catalogue. (6) See his comments in Thieme-Becker *Lexikon*, XXX, p. 466 (*ad vocem*). (7) Notes on the costume kindly contributed by Stella M. Pearce in the Gallery archives. She relates the costume of No. 4206 to that in such portraits as the Mielich *Young Woman* (Berlin), dated 1543, and a *Duchess of Saxony* by Cranach the Younger, dated 1549. (8) As by Lucas Cranach the Younger. Abel's MS. addition to that catalogue calls it School of the younger Holbein. (9) As School of the younger Holbein. (10) *I.e.* Lange's catalogue; see the note 3 here. (11) As by an imitator of Holbein. (12) As by Seisenegger.

SOUTH GERMAN School, XV century

4901   S. JOHN ON PATMOS

The saint is shown writing; beside him his eagle on a closed book.
Oak, painted surface, $16\frac{7}{8} \times 17\frac{1}{4}$ (0·428 × 0·438).
In fair condition but there is some flaking and cracking over most of the panel.

S. John's symbol of the eagle is derived from Ezekiel, i, 4–10.
No. 4901 is obviously under strong Netherlandish influence but seems to be South German in origin, despite the use of oak for the support. The picture was originally supposed to be Netherlandish but Friedländer pointed out its correct School and dated it *ca.* 1460[1]; later he amended this date to *ca.* 1470.[2] The picture was published by R. Schapire as quite close to Konrad Witz[3] and recently Stange has tentatively associated it with the style of the Witz follower, the Master of Sierenz,[4] who was probably active at Bâle.
However, O. Fischer seems to have rejected any specific association with Witz and he suggested an origin in Alsace, possibly Strasbourg.[5] O. Benesch[6] drew attention to the Austrian connection and linked No. 4901 with a picture of the Salzburg School (at Munich).[7] Benesch suggests that No. 4901 is from the Austrian 'Vorlande' about 1470: that is, from the South German region which included part of Alsace and the area round Bâle. It is doubtful if a more precise attribution is possible.

PROVENANCE: Chamberlin Collection, Hove; exhibited at the Guildhall Netherlandish exhibition, 1906 (no. 23)[8]; at the Burlington Fine Arts Club, 1934-5 (no. 26).[9] Bequeathed by W. B. Chamberlin, 1937.

REPRODUCTION: By Schapire, *loc. cit.*, and Stange, *loc. cit.*

REFERENCES: (1) See his review of the 1906 Guildhall exhibition in *Repertorium für Kunstwissenschaft*, 1906, p. 576. (2) Letter of 1937 in the Gallery archives; in a further letter of the same year, Friedländer mentions seeing other South German pictures on oak. (3) See her article in *Monatshefte für Kunstwissenschaft*, 1908, pp. 909 ff. (4) A. Stange, *Deutsche Malerei der Gotik*: IV, *Südwestdeutschland* . . . 1951, pp. 152-3. (5) Letter of 1938 in the Gallery archives. (6) Record in the Gallery archives of notes made by Benesch in 1939. (7) Munich, 1930 catalogue, no. 8781 (pl. 154) as 'Salzburgisch um 1470'. (8) As unknown Flemish; according to the *Supplement to the 1929 Catalogue*, 1939, p. 17, the picture was once attributed to Justus van Ghent. (9) As South German School, late fifteenth century.

SOUTH GERMAN SCHOOL, XVI century

1232 PORTRAIT OF A MAN

Nearly waist length, facing left. He holds two pinks.
Beech, painted area, $19\frac{5}{8} \times 15\frac{3}{8}$ (0·499 × 0·391).
In good condition under discoloured varnish.

In the 1929 catalogue as by Baldung which is clearly wrong; it had earlier been called Aldegrever. Some other attributions have been made, but none known to the present writer is fully convincing. Hugelshofer attributed the picture and its pendant (see further below) to Christoph Bockstorffer.[1] There are no known portraits by this painter and the affinities between his other pictures and No. 1232 are very slight. Benesch suggested that the picture is by the Master A.G. who was conceivably active at Augsburg but whose connection with the Danubian School is strong.[2] The Danubian air of No. 1232 is its most obvious feature and there are some affinities with portraits by Wertinger and Ostendorfer.

The pendant *Portrait of a Woman* by the same hand is in the Oscar Reinhart collection at Winterthur[3]; the pair are perhaps marriage portraits. A date for the pictures in the decade 1530-40 seems probable.

PROVENANCE: In the Ralph Bernal sale, London, 13 March (8th day), 1855 (lot 916)[4] bought by Anthony. In the J. Whatman sale, London, 2 July 1887 (lot 34)[5] bought out of the Walker Fund for the National Gallery.

REPRODUCTION: *Illustrations, Continental Schools*, 1937, p. 15.

REFERENCES: (1) Letter of 1931 in the Gallery archives. He speaks there of a forthcoming article on Bockstorffer which the present writer has not succeeded in tracing and which perhaps never appeared. For some comment on Bockstorffer, see H. Rott in *Quellen und Forschungen zur Süd-Westdeutschen und Schweizerischen Kunstgeschichte im XV und XVI Jahrhundert*, I, 1933, pp. 80 ff. (2) Notes by Benesch in 1939, recorded in the Gallery archives. The Master A.G. is named from a *Portrait of a Man* (Liechtenstein Collection) so monogrammed and dated 1540: see further O. Benesch in Prussian *Jahrbuch*, 1933, pp. 250 ff. (3) As South German, *ca.* 1515, in the exhibition catalogue, *Sammlung Oscar Reinhart*, Berne, 1939–40, p. 31; the attribution retained in later exhibitions of the collection. (4) As *A Duke of Saxony* by Cranach. Lot 914, bought by Morant, is the Reinhart pendant. Both pictures bear similar seals (with the monogram CM) on the reverse, indicating that they were together in a collection before acquisition by Bernal. (5) As by Holbein.

SWABIAN School, XV century

722 PORTRAIT OF A WOMAN OF THE HOFER FAMILY

Bust length, to the right; she holds a sprig of forget-me-not. On her headdress a fly.

Inscribed at the top: *GEBORNE HOFERIN.*

Silver fir (*abies alba*) painted area, $21\frac{1}{8} \times 15\frac{7}{8}$ (0.537 × 0.408).

In good condition under discoloured varnish; there are a few small damages.

The name Hofer is too common in Southern Germany and Switzerland for any useful clue to be contained in the inscription on No. 722—especially as no reference is made to the sitter's married name. The fly on the headdress has probably no symbolic purpose but is more likely introduced as a piece of *trompe l'œil*[1]; it is used illusionistically in this way by Crivelli and by Dürer.[2]

Although No. 722 has been rather variously attributed, there is agreement that the picture is Swabian in origin. Nineteenth century attributions of it are largely irrelevant. In the 1929 catalogue it appears simply as of the German School and a misleading reference is made to a portrait by Schongauer (in fact by Wohlgemut) at Cassel. Hugelshofer called it Styrian.[3] Gerstenberg published it as by the House Book Master.[4] Friedländer's opinion that it was Southern German *ca.* 1470 is recorded.[5] Deusch suggested the same date and attributed it to the Nuremberg School,[6] with which it has affinities.

Buchner has recently published it with a query as by the Master of the Sterzing wings, an attribution he has apparently believed in for many years.[7] The attribution is accepted by Stange.[8] The analogies between that Master's work and No. 722 are very striking, but do not seem in the final analysis quite convincing. Buchner's dating of the picture, somewhere about 1460, fits in very well with the Sterzing Master's activity; but it seems rather too early. His dating is specifically rejected by Strieder who points out that the costume of No. 722 appears in Nuremberg pictures of considerably later in the century.[9] Pictures in which a very similar headdress is shown occur at least until Schaffner.[10]

The Sterzing Master's influence does seem present in No. 722, and other pictures from Ulm at the period show very similar handling.[11]

PROVENANCE: In the collection of Prince Ludwig Kraft Ernst von Oettingen-Wallerstein; at Schloss Wallerstein by 1826.[12] Exhibited for sale at Kensington Palace, 1848 (no. 65),[13] bought with the rest of the collection by the Prince Consort. At Kensington Palace, 1854.[14] Presented by Queen Victoria, at the Prince Consort's wish, 1863.

REPRODUCTION: *Illustrations, Continental Schools*, 1937, p. 136.

REFERENCES: (1) A fly appears very similarly on the woman's headdress in a double portrait by the Master of Frankfort; cf. the reproduction in I. Bergström, *Dutch Still-Life Painting in the Seventeenth Century*, 1956, p. 11. It is quite true that the fly has sometimes significance as a mortality symbol (through the idea of disease) but that does not seem the intention behind its appearance in either of these portraits. (2) Cf. the note by E. Panofsky, *Early Netherlandish Painting*, 1953, I, pp. 488/9. (3) W. Hugelshofer in *Belvedere*, VIII, 1929, pp. 417 ff., associating No. 722 with a picture then at Graz (now Thyssen collection, Lugano). (4) K. Gerstenberg in *Repertorium für Kunstwissenschaft*, 1931, pp. 65 ff.; for an unfavourable comment on this attribution see the House Book Master entry in Thieme-Becker *Lexikon*, XXXVII, p. 141, col. 1. (5) Note of Friedländer's opinion in 1932 is in the Gallery archives. (6) W. R. Deusch, *Deutsche Malerei des Fünfzehnten Jahrhunderts*, 1936, p. 30. Some further bibliographical references are in E. Buchner, *Das deutsche Bildnis der Spätgotik und der frühen Dürerzeit*, 1953, p. 194 (under no. 54). (7) Buchner, *op. cit.*, p. 64. (8) A. Stange, *Deutsche Malerei der Gotik*: VIII, *Schwaben in der Zeit von 1450 bis 1500*, 1957, p. 9. (9) See P. Strieder's review of Buchner, *op. cit.*, in *Kunstchronik*, 1954, pp. 47–8. Notes on the costume by Stella Mary Pearce (in the Gallery archives) also suggest a later date, in the late sixties or early seventies. (10) Compare for instance the woman supporting the Virgin in the Wettenhausen *Christ taking leave of His Mother* (Munich) of 1523–4: reproduced in J. Baum, *Ulmer Kunst*, 1911, p. 82. (11) See for example, Buchner, *op. cit.*, pl. 197, and text under No. 196, pp. 170 ff. (12) 1826(?) lithographed catalogue, no. 74 as Israel von Mecheln: same attribution and number in 1827 manuscript catalogue (photostats in Gallery archives of originals at Munich). (13) As Israel von Mecheln. (14) Waagen's catalogue, 1854, no. 24 (p. 17), not Israel van Meckenem and apparently as Master of the Lyversberg Passion.

TYROLESE SCHOOL, XV century

4190   THE DORMITION OF THE VIRGIN

S. Peter (?) incenses the Virgin; left of him an Apostle holding a palm.[1] In the foreground, a kneeling Franciscan (?), beside whom a scroll inscribed: *trahe me post te asumptio marie*. The book held by the Apostle (S. John?) at the left inscribed on the left-hand page: *laudate pu | eri domi | num laudate nom | en domi | ni excelsus | super om | nes;* on the right-hand page: *gentes do | minus et | super celos | gloria ei | us asolis | ortu [us] que | ad ocas [um] | laudab [ile]*.

Pine,[2] 35 × 28¼ (0·889 × 0·718), painted on all sides up to the edge of the frame which seems original.

In good condition; there are a few very minor damages.

The verses inscribed on the Apostle's book are from Psalm CXIII (Vulgate, 112), 1/4 and part of verse 3 (in that order).

According to the Golden Legend the Apostles were miraculously summoned together for the Dormition of the Virgin; it seems an oddity in No. 4190 that there are thirteen Apostles. The figure introduced into the scene wears a grey habit and is probably a Franciscan, possibly the donor of the picture. No. 4190 is perhaps part of an altarpiece.

The picture has been very variously attributed, but recent scholars have agreed that it is of Tyrolese origin. According to the 1929 catalogue it was at one time attributed to Ottaviano Nelli; in the 1929 catalogue attributed to the Spanish School, fifteenth century—perhaps Valencian. It was hesitatingly connected by Post with a Valencian painter (in the circle of Nicolau and Marzal de Sas).[3] Morassi apparently originally thought the picture to be Tyrolese[4] but later seems to have accepted it as Catalan.[5]. J. Puig y Cadafalch finds similarities with the style of Lluis Borrassa.[6] The affinities with Spanish painting are superficial and misleading; and the picture has been excluded by Neil MacLaren from his catalogue of Spanish pictures in the Gallery, indicating instead the attribution here.

Benesch suggested that it was by the painter of some fifteenth century frescoes in the cloister of the cathedral at Bressanone (Brixen).[7] It is attributed by Salvini to the School of Trento, and he points out resemblances to the altarpiece at S. Sigismondo, Pusteria, and the St. Korbinian triptych.[8] Baldass has commented on the picture, agreeing that it originates in the region of the Tyrol and relating it rather to S. Sigismondo than to the Bressanone frescoes.[9] Finally, in support of the attribution here, it is worth noting that the provenance is from a Trento collection and that the species of wood on which No. 4190 is painted is apparently not found in Spain but does occur in Switzerland, Italy and the Tyrol.[10]

PROVENANCE: In the Vambianchi collection, Trento[11]; presented by the 1st Viscount Rothermere, 1926.

REPRODUCTION: *Illustrations, Continental Schools*, 1937, p. 341.

REFERENCES: (1) The palm is part of the legend of the Virgin's Dormition. When she prayed for death an angel appeared and gave her a palm, prophesying her dormition; this palm she afterwards gave to one of the Apostles. (2) Of *Pinus cembra* type, according to Dr. E. W. J. Phillips, Forest Products Research Laboratory, 1947 (letters in the Gallery archives). (3) Cf. C. R. Post, *History of Spanish Painting*, III, 1930, p. 89. This painter executed the retable, said to have come from San Juan del Hospital at Valencia, which is divided between the Metropolitan Museum and the Hispanic Society, New York; the personality was later christened 'the Gil Master' by Post, *op. cit.*, VII, part 2, 1938, p. 79. (4) Letter of 1930 in the Gallery archives. (5) Cf. A. Morassi, *Storia della Pittura nella Venezia Tridentina*, 1934, pp. 442–3. (6) Letter of 1938 in the Gallery archives. (7) Letter of 1939 in the Gallery archives: for these frescoes, see Morassi, *op. cit.*, figs 274–8. (8) See his article in *Le Arti*, 1940–1, pp. 113 and 115. (9) Letters of 1949 in the Gallery archives. For the *Dormition of the Virgin* at S. Sigismondo, see O. Pächt, *Österreichische Tafelmalerei der Gotik*, 1929, pl. 57. (10) See the note 2 above. (11) Published as such by Salvini, *op. cit.*, p. 113.

JACOB WEIER
Active 1645–died 1670

Or *Weyer*, but the form above is more commonly used by the painter. He is the author of a number of camp and battle pictures, and some genre pictures. Two pictures are dated 1645 (one of them No. 1470 below). He is apparently the Jacob Weier who was made official painter in Hamburg in 1648 and died there, 8 May 1670.[1] The evidence is very strong that he was trained in Holland, and most of his pictures are pastiches of Dutch painters; signed pictures, fairly surely earlier than No. 1470 below, are in the manner of Palamedes Palamedesz.[2] (Delft; 1607–38).

Weier has sometimes been identified, wrongly, with Johann Matthias Weyer of Hamburg (ca. 1620–90?) who was also a battle painter and who apparently also studied in Holland.[3] It seems quite clear that this painter is a different personality.[4] He is sometimes called Jacob Matthias Weyer, but this seems merely part of the confusion and incorrect.

REFERENCES: (1) See the detailed entry in F. Schlie's Schwerin catalogue, 1882, pp. 686 ff. (under Weier). (2) A Palamedesz. pastiche *Battle scene* (signed in cursive *J. Weier*) in Anonymous sale, Christie, 4 July 1952 (lot 42). Pastiches in a Wouwermans manner are not uncommon (cf. No. 1470). A signed *Halt of Soldiers* in the Tollemache collection (certainly by Jacob Weier) is in yet a third manner, vaguely that of the Haarlem School, and with some affinity to Thomas Wyck. (3) Cf. the entry in Thieme-Becker *Lexikon*, XXXV, p. 479, which incorrectly states that *Christ carrying the Cross* and the *Hawking Party* previously at Schwerin and now in the Kunsthalle, Hamburg, are signed *Jacob M. Weyer*; the former alone is signed, *IACOB WEIER*. That the two painters are two different personalities is early established by Brunswick inventories; cf. the Brunswick catalogue, 1900, nos. 568–70 by Johann Matthias Weyer, no. 571 Jakob Weyer. The entry in Thieme-Becker, *loc. cit.*, gives no good reason for rejecting this evidence. (4) A drawing initialled *MW* (in ligature) in the Albertina ascribed to him; cf. *Die Zeichnungen der deutschen Schulen*, 1933, No. 717.

1470 CAVALRY ATTACKED BY INFANTRY

Signed below the point of the sword of the man kneeling in the right foreground: *I WEIER | 1645* (very faint).

Oil on oak, $15\frac{1}{8} \times 23\frac{1}{16}$ (0·384 × 0·602).

In quite good condition. Worn in a number of places, especially in the figures on the right. Cleaned in 1952.

No. 1470 is a typical example of Weier's pastiches in the manner of Wouwermans. As has been mentioned in the biography above, it is one of two pictures dated 1645 which are at present the earliest firm evidence for Weier's activity.

PROVENANCE: Apparently in a late eighteenth- or early nineteenth-century French(?) sale.[1] Presented by Sir Augustus Wollaston Franks, 1896.

REPRODUCTION: *Illustrations, Continental Schools*, 1937, p. 397.

REFERENCE: (1) In the Gallery archives is a cutting from an unidentified sale catalogue, apparently late eighteenth or early nineteenth century, which was formerly stuck on the back of the panel: 'WEIER. 1615. [sic]|49 Corps de cavalerie enveloppé par l'in-|fanterie, les assaillants se battent à bout port-|ant, les premiers voyant leur perte certaine|se défendent avec intrépidité; ce tableau de|la meilleure couleur est touché avec esprit. H.|14 p., 1. 22. B.'

APPENDIX I:

RECONSTRUCTION OF THE CENTRAL PANEL OF THE LIESBORN HIGH ALTARPIECE

IN DISCUSSION under Nos. 259–261, Master of Liesborn, it has been remarked that the central panel of the high altarpiece at Liesborn Abbey was a Crucifixion with saints and angels. Of this large panel only seven fragments survive; from these it is apparent that the subject was treated meditatively rather than historically. It seems clear that the thieves on their crosses were not included, and in place of the usual Westphalian depiction of a crowded Calvary scene the subject was treated in a manner more typical of the Cologne School: with a plain gold background, little if any landscape, and saints about the Cross chosen for their appropriateness not to the theme but to the circumstances of the commission. A comparable but earlier example, on a smaller scale, is Lochner's *Crucifixion* at Nuremberg.

The accompanying diagram shows a reconstruction of the central panel which is broadly likely to be correct. The approximate size of the original panel can be deduced from the fortunate survival intact of one panel from the wings (No. 256); it probably measured about 78 × 108 inches (1·982 × 2·744), unframed.

It is not established if the seven surviving pieces of this constitute in fragmentary state all the figures originally included in the scene. Since no figure survives totally intact, the exact placing of some portions may be in doubt but others are quite sure. From the gold tooling on Nos. 259–261, it can be proved that they must have occupied positions at the top and side edges respectively; a double border of such tooling is usual, but only one appears on these pictures, indicating that their present edges are not the original edges of the central panel. These three fragments establish the composition and effect in general terms of the scene: Christ crucified in the centre, flanked by the Virgin and S. John, accompanied at the left by SS. Cosmas and Damian, at the right by SS. Scholastica and Benedict.

The remaining four fragments of angels are in the Landesmuseum, Münster. The place of only one of these, the largest, can be fixed with absolute certainty: at the bottom left of the fragment of the *Head of Christ* (No. 259) is a portion of angel's wing which accords with the right-hand wing of the angel in this fragment, and the two fragments can be juxtaposed as shown here. The angel, who holds a chalice, is drawing away from the wound in Christ's side. Two fragments, each of the same size, show angels in profile holding up chalices and they were probably placed facing into the centre, at either arm of the Cross; alternatively, they were in the same position but faced outwards, drawing away from the Cross. The smallest fragment is of a weeping angel; the fragment is sufficient to show that the left arm was extended, and almost certainly this angel too held a chalice—placed at Christ's feet.

From the accompanying diagram, it can be seen that a curious feature of the central panel was the amount of space on either side of the Cross. There were clearly no other saints included and it is unlikely that there were further mourning angels. On analogy with Cologne practice, it would not be unusual if this space was partly occupied by a donor or donors (Lochner's *Crucifixion* may again be compared). The matter does not seem susceptible of proof, but the suggestion may be put forward for consideration.

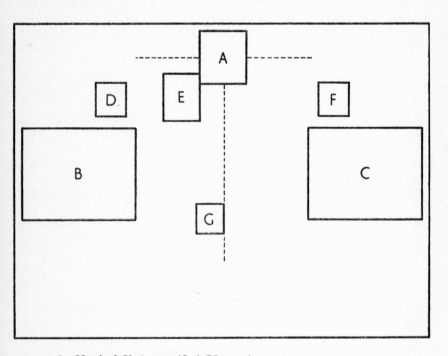

A. Head of Christ crucified (No. 259)
B. SS. Cosmas and Damian and the Virgin (No. 261)
C. SS. John the Evangelist, Scholastica and Benedict (No. 260)
D. Angel facing left (?), holding a chalice (Münster)
E. Angel holding a chalice (Münster)
F. Angel facing right (?), holding a chalice (Münster)
G. Weeping angel (Münster)

APPENDIX II:

THE KRÜGER COLLECTION

THE MAJORITY of the Krüger collection was bought from the owner by the Gallery in 1854. A catalogue of the collection had been published at Minden in 1848 (a copy of this very rare item is in the Gallery archives), and a few pictures from the collection were disposed of by Krüger between then and the purchase in 1854.

Very little is known about Carl Wilhelm August Krüger (1797–1868) and the biographical information here is derived from the article by W. K. Schmidt in *Mindener Heimatblätter*, June/August 1953, pp. 62 ff., a copy of which, kindly sent by the Stadtarchiv, Minden, is in the Gallery archives; that article is probably the first to be devoted to him. Some information about him is also contained in the Stadtarchiv, Aachen, and has kindly been sent by Dr. Poll. Krüger was born at Stettin, 11 June 1797, and held various legal posts at Frankfort, Münster, Minden, and Aachen; he retired from service, 1859, and died at Münster, 22 December 1868.

It seems likely that his collection, which consisted almost entirely of early German, mainly Westphalian, pictures, was chiefly formed in the 1820's. It is first commented on by Passavant in 1833. In 1835 at the time of moving from Aachen to Münster, Krüger mentions the packing of his collection ('Bibliothek, Kupferstiche, Gemälde') as the reason for his request for leave of several weeks.

The collection was inspected at Minden by William Dyce, R.A., late in 1853, or perhaps early in 1854, with a view to its acquisition for the nation. In April 1854 the sixty-four pictures which remained of the collection were purchased. In October of the same year seventeen were placed on exhibition. It was agreed that among the collection were pictures of not sufficiently high standard to retain and by a Bill of 1856 (19° & 20° *Victoriæ*, Cap. 29, of 23 June 1856), the Trustees' powers were extended to allow sale of pictures not given or bequeathed. In January 1857, ten Krüger pictures from among those not on exhibition were selected for loan to the National Gallery of Ireland (those chosen printed in Appendix 3 to the National Gallery Report of 1857). On 14 February 1857, the remaining thirty-seven pictures were sold at Messrs. Christie, along with two pictures from the Galvagna collection. A return to a House of Commons Order of 24 February 1857, for a full account of the expenditure on, and disposal of, the Krüger collection, is dated 26 February 1857.

The Krüger catalogue of 1848 and the National Gallery sale catalogue of 1857 have been reprinted by R. Fritz in *Westfalen*, 1951, pp. 87 ff. For convenience the relevant portion of the 1857 sale catalogue is printed here, so as to record exactly what Krüger pictures originally belonged to the Gallery. The prices are added from MS. annotations in a copy of the sale catalogue in the Gallery archives and the opportunity has been taken to correct some of the prices as given by Fritz. For the present whereabouts of some of these pictures, see his article *loc. cit.*

"PORTION OF THE KRÜGER COLLECTION

The descriptions are from the German Catalogue, published at Minden, 1848. *The numbers in that Catalogue are added to each description.*

		£	s.	d.
Unknown, 14th century	3 St. Stephen. *From the Convent Church of Wormeln, near Warburg.* Part I.—1	1	15	0
Unknown, end of 14th century	4 Panel, with three subjects—The Forbidden Fruit, the Fall, the Expulsion from Paradise. *From the Church at Schildesche, near Bielefeld.* Part I.—2	1	2	0
Ditto	5 The Annunciation. *From the same Church.* Part I.—5	8	15	0
Unknown, end of 14th century	6 Panel, with three subjects—The Adoration of the Kings, the Circumcision, the Flight into Egypt. *From the same Church.* Part I.—3	5	5	0
Ditto	7 Panel, with three subjects—The Betrayal of Christ, Christ crowned with thorns, the Flagellation. *From the same Church.* Part I.—6	5	0	0
Ditto	8 Panel, with three subjects—Christ before Pilate, Christ bearing his cross, the Crucifixion. *From the same Church.* Part I.—4	4	10	0
Ditto	9 Panel, with three subjects—The Ascension, the Descent of the Holy Ghost, the Last Judgment. *From the same Church.* Part I.—7	4	0	0
Earlier Liesborn School	10 The Ascension. *From a Chapel at Lippstadt.* Part I.—18	21	0	0
Ditto	11 St. Barbara. *From the same Chapel.* Part I.—21	3	0	0
Ditto	12 St. Agnes. *From the same Chapel.* Part I.—22	3	5	0
Later Liesborn School	13 Mary Magdalen, and St. John the Evangelist. *From the Convent Church at Liesborn.* Part I.—23			
Ditto	14 St. James the Elder. *From the same Church.* Part I.—24	4	0	0
Unknown	15 Christ bearing his Cross. *From a chapel at Munster.* Part I.—31	22	0	0
Ditto	16 The Entombment. *From the same Chapel.* Part I—32	2	15	0
The Meister von Soest	17 The Virgin and Child in glory. *From the Convent Church at Soest.* Part I.—33	13	10	0

8—G.S.

			£	s.	d.
The Meister von Soest	18	The Annunciation. *From the same Church.* Part I.—34	1	15	0
Ditto	19	St. John the Evangelist. *From the same Church.* Part I.—35	2	10	0
Ditto	20	St. Matthew. *From the same Church.* Part I.—36	4	10	0
The later Meister von Liesborn, 16th century	21	The Last Judgment. *From the Convent Church at Liesborn, or Marienfeld.* Part I.—38	14	14	0
Ditto	22	Christ before Caiaphas. *From the same Church.* Part I.—43	21	10	0
Ditto	23	Christ derided. *From the same Church.* Part I.—40	10	0	0
Ditto	24	The Flagellation. *From the same Church.* Part I.—41	9	19	6
Ditto	25	Christ bearing his cross. *From the same Church.* Part I.—42	5	15	0
Ditto	26	The Resurrection. *From the same Church.* Part I.—45	13	13	0
Ditto	27	The Ascension. *From the same Church.* Part I.—44	9	19	6
Liesborn School	28	The Annunciation. *From the Convent Church at Liesborn.* Part I.—48	1	4	0
Ditto	29	The Nativity. *From the same Church.* Part I.—49	1	18	0
Ditto	30	The Adoration of the Kings. *From the same Church.* Part I.—50	2	10	0
Ditto	31	The Presentation in the Temple. *From the same Church.* Part I.—51	3	0	0
Ditto	32	The Three Maries. *From the same Church.* Part I.—52	2	15	0

LATER SCHOOLS.

			£	s.	d.
School of Albert Dürer	33	The Crucifixion. Part II.—1	2	8	0
Unknown	34	St. Jerome with a scull (*sic*). Part II.—2		12	0
Ditto	35	A small portrait of a Flemish Counsellor —*on copper.* Part II.—3	1	8	0
Unknown	36	Portrait of the wife—*on copper.* Part II—4	1	11	6
School of William of Cologne	37	Head of a saint. Part II.—6	1	3	0
School of Lucas Cranach	38	Judith with the head of Holofernes. Part II.—10	3	8	0
MEISTER VON CORVEY	39	The Crucifixion, with six saints below. *From the Abbey Church of Corvey, near Höxter.* Part I.—30 "	18	7	6

LIST OF ATTRIBUTIONS CHANGED FROM THE CATALOGUE OF 1929 AND THE SUPPLEMENT OF 1939

Note: Changes of terminology not affecting the status of a picture (*e.g.* 'Circle of' in place of 'School of') are not recorded.

Previous Attribution	*Inventory Number*	*Present Attribution*
MASTER OF WERDEN	250	Studio of the MASTER OF THE LIFE OF THE VIRGIN
MASTER OF WERDEN	251	Studio of the MASTER OF THE LIFE OF THE VIRGIN
MASTER OF WERDEN	252	Studio of the MASTER OF THE LIFE OF THE VIRGIN
MASTER OF WERDEN	253	Studio of the MASTER OF THE LIFE OF THE VIRGIN
MASTER OF LIESBORN	254	Circle of the MASTER OF LIESBORN
MASTER OF LIESBORN	255	Circle of the MASTER OF LIESBORN
WESTPHALIAN School, XVI century	263	MASTER OF CAPPENBERG
Ascribed to MASTER WILHELM	687	Circle of the MASTER OF S. VERONICA
GERMAN School, XV century	722	SWABIAN School, XV century
School of SCHONGAUER	723	Style of SCHONGAUER
Ascribed to MENGS	1099	Anton Raphael MENGS
Hans BALDUNG	1232	SOUTH GERMAN School, XVI century
Albrecht DÜRER	1938	Ascribed to DÜRER
WESTPHALIAN School, XVI century	2151	Circle of the MASTER OF LIESBORN
WESTPHALIAN School, XVI century	2154	MASTER OF CAPPENBERG
GERMAN School	2156	GERMAN(?) School, XVII century
GERMAN School	2157	Ascribed to the GERMAN School
WESTPHALIAN School, XVI century	2160	NORTH GERMAN School
Christoph AMBERGER	2604	AUGSBURG(?) School, XVI century
GERMAN School	2670	COLOGNE School, XV century
Jan LYS	3571	Johann Carl LOTH
FRANCO–RHENISH School, XV century	3662	AUSTRIAN School, XV century
DUTCH School, XV century	3665	Circle of the MASTER OF THE S. URSULA LEGEND
SPANISH School, XV century	4190	TYROLESE School, XV century
GERMAN School, XV century	4901	SOUTH GERMAN School, XV century

INDEX TO PORTRAITS, PROFANE
AND GENRE SUBJECTS

* An asterisk denotes that the figure or scene is not a principal part of the picture.

INDEX TO RELIGIOUS SUBJECTS

A: SAINTS

S. Agnes:
Circle of the Master of Liesborn, No. 262
*Circle of the Master of Liesborn, No. 2153

S. Ambrose:
Circle of the Master of Liesborn, No. 254

S. Andrew:
Circle of the Master of Liesborn, No. 262

S. Anne:
Circle of the Master of Liesborn, No. 262

S. Augustine:
Circle of the Master of Liesborn, No. 255
Studio of the Master of the Life of the Virgin, No. 251

S. Benedict:
Master of Liesborn, No. 260
Circle of the Master of Liesborn, No. 262
Studio of the Master of the Life of the Virgin, No. 250

S. Bernard(?)
Studio of the Master of the Life of the Virgin, No. 250

S. Catherine of Alexandria:
Lochner, No. 705

S. Christopher:
German(?) School, XVII century, No. 2156

S. Cosmas:
Master of Liesborn, No. 261

S. Damian:
Master of Liesborn, No. 261

S. Dorothy:
Master of S. Bartholomew, No. 707
Circle of the Master of Liesborn, No. 2152

S. Exuperius:
Circle of the Master of Liesborn, No. 254

S. Gereon(?):
Studio of the Master of the Life of the Virgin, No. 251

S. Giles:
Studio of the Master of the Life of the Virgin, No. 250

S. Gregory:
Lochner, No. 705
Circle of the Master of Liesborn, No. 255

S. Hubert:
Studio of the Master of the Life of the Virgin, Nos. 251, 252, 253

S. Jerome:
Lochner, No. 705
Circle of the Master of Liesborn, No. 254
Studio of the Master of the Life of the Virgin, No. 250

S. John the Baptist:
Mengs, No. 1099
Elsheimer, No. 3904

S. John the Evangelist:
Baldung, No. 1427
Bruyn, No. 3903
Lochner, No. 705
Master of the Aachen Altarpiece, No. 1049
Master of Liesborn, No. 260
Circle of the Master of Liesborn, No. 262
Master of S. Bartholomew, No. 707
South German School, XV century, No. 4901
Tyrolese School, XVI century, No. 4190

S. Joseph:
Master of the Life of the Virgin, No. 706

S. Lawrence:
Elsheimer, No. 1014
Circle of the Master of the S. Ursula Legend, No. 3665

S. Ludger(?)
Studio of the Master of the Life of the Virgin, No. 251

S. Margaret:
Circle of the Master of Liesborn, No. 2153

S. Mary Magdalene:
Bruyn, No. 3903
Circle of the Master of Liesborn,
No. 262

S. Matthew:
Lochner, No. 705

S. Maurice:
Circle of the Master of Liesborn,
No. 255

S. Michael:
Circle of Pacher, No. 5786

S. Paul:
Elsheimer, No. 3535
*Studio of the Master of the Life of
the Virgin, No. 253

S. Peter:
Elsheimer, No. 3904
*Studio of the Master of the Life of
the Virgin, No. 253
Master of S. Bartholomew, No. 707
Tyrolese School, XV century, No.
4190

S. Raphael:
Elsheimer, No. 1424

S. Scholastica:
Master of Liesborn, No. 260
Circle of the Master of Liesborn,
No. 262

S. Veronica:
Circle of the Master of S. Veronica,
No. 687

B: OTHER RELIGIOUS SUBJECTS

Note: Christ is not indexed separately, except in scenes of his life where the
name is the first word of the title (e.g. Christ carrying the Cross). The Virgin
is indexed separately only where the subject is not a scene of her life otherwise
indexed.

Abel:
*Master of the Life of the Virgin,
No. 706

Abraham:
*Master of Liesborn, No. 260
*Master of the Life of the Virgin,
No. 706

Adoration of the Kings:
Master of Liesborn, No. 258

Annunciation:
Master of Liesborn, No. 256
*Circle of the Master of Liesborn,
No. 255
*Circle of Pacher, No. 5786

Baptism of Christ:
Elsheimer, No. 3904

Cain:
*Master of the Life of the Virgin,
No. 706

Christ before Pilate:
Master of Cappenberg, No. 2154

Christ carrying the Cross:
North German School, No. 2160

Christ falling under the Cross:
*Master of the Aachen Altarpiece,
No. 1049

Coronation of the Virgin:
Master of Cappenberg, No. 263

Crucifixion:
Master of the Aachen Altarpiece,
No. 1049
*Master of Liesborn, No. 259
Circle of the Master of Liesborn,
No. 262

David:
*Master of Liesborn, No. 257

Deposition:
*Master of the Aachen Altarpiece,
No. 1049

Dormition of the Virgin:
Tyrolese School, XV century, No.
4190

God the Father (see also Trinity):
*Style of Dürer, No. 5592
*Elsheimer, No. 3904
*Master of Liesborn, No. 256
*Studio of the Master of the Life of
the Virgin, No. 253

Holofernes:
Liss, No. 4597

Isaac:
*Master of Liesborn, No. 260
*Master of the Life of the Virgin,
No. 706

INDEX OF PREVIOUS OWNERS

Probable or possible owners mentioned in the Provenance entries are included.
The date of anonymous sales only is given below.

Abel:
Seisenegger, No. 4206

Albert, Prince:
Lochner, No. 705
Master of the Life of the Virgin,
No. 706
Master of S. Bartholomew, No. 707
Style of Schongauer, No. 723
Swabian School, XV century, No.
722

Anonymous sale, London, 27 March
1779:
Elsheimer, No. 3904

Anonymous sale, London, 25 April
1812:
Elsheimer, No. 3904

Anthony:
South German School, XVI century, No. 1232

Arundel (Thomas Howard), Earl/
Countess of:
Holbein, No. 2475

Ashburton, Louisa, Lady:
Ascribed to Dürer, No. 1938

Bammeville, E. Joly de:
Baldung, No. 245

Basville, Marquis de:
Holbein, No. 1314

Beckford, William (Snr. and Jnr.):
Elsheimer, No. 1424

Bernal, Ralph:
South German School, XVI century, No. 1232

Böhler (Munich):
Seisenegger, No. 4206

Boisserée, Sulpiz and Melchior:
Lochner, No. 705
Master of the Life of the Virgin,
No. 706

Bowden:
Elsheimer, No. 3904

Buchanan, William:
Holbein, No. 1314

Burns, Walter:
Elsheimer, No. 3535

Campe, Friedrich:
Cranach, No. 291

Carlisle, Rosalind, Countess of:
Cranach, No. 2925

Carter:
Baldung, No. 1427

Cassirer (Berlin):
Austrian School, XV century, No.
3662

Cessac, Marquis de:
Holbein, No. 1314

Chamberlin, W. B.:
South German School, XV century,
No. 4901

Charles I, King:
Ascribed to Dürer, No. 1938

Colnaghi, Messrs. P. & D.:
Holbein, No. 2475

Cologne, SS. John and Cordula:
Lochner, No. 705

Cologne, S. Lawrence:
Circle of the Master of S. Veronica,
No. 687

Cologne, S. Ursula:
Master of the Life of the Virgin,
No. 706

Cook, Sir Francis/Sir Frederick:
Style of Dürer, No. 5592

Darcy, 3rd Lord:
Holbein, No. 2475

Dermer:
Elsheimer, No. 3904

Desvignes, P. H.:
Style of Dürer, No. 5592

Dethier:
Lochner, No. 705

Dinteville, Jean de:
Holbein, No. 1314

Dixon:
Master of the Aachen Altarpiece,
No. 1049

Dollar, James W.:
Liss, No. 4597

NUMERICAL INDEX OF PAINTINGS
INCLUDED IN THIS CATALOGUE